'It is a truth universally acknowledged, that a bum in possession of some gas, must be in want of a fart.'

Jane Austink

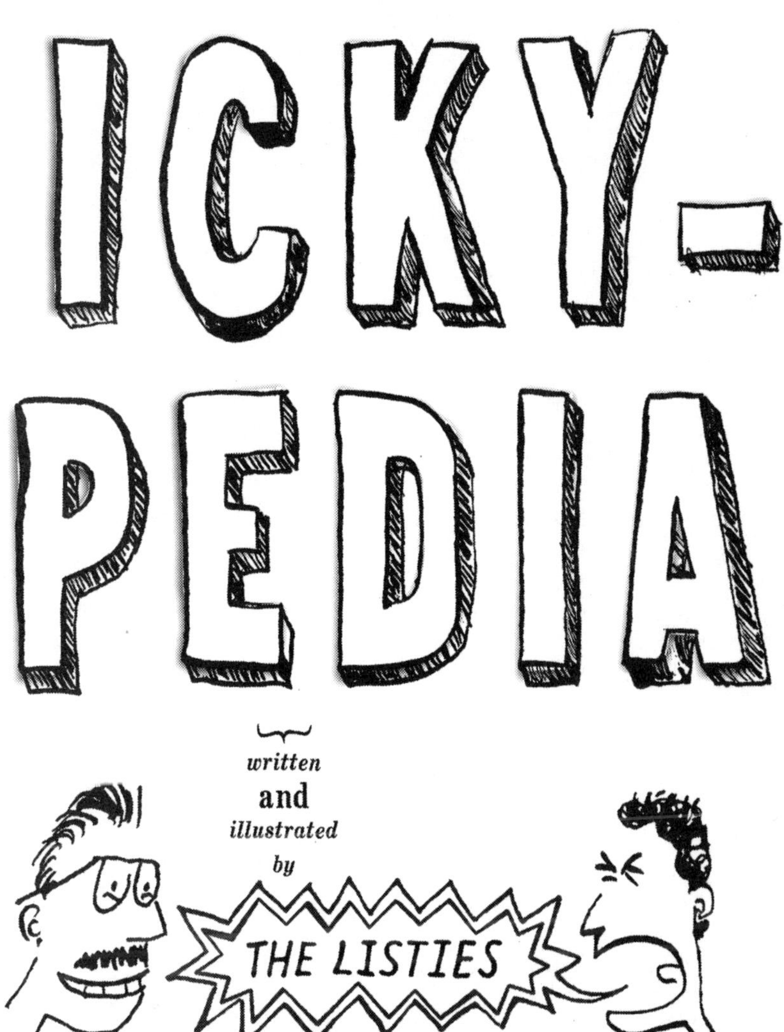

Puffin Books

THE COUNTING BOOK by THE LISTIES

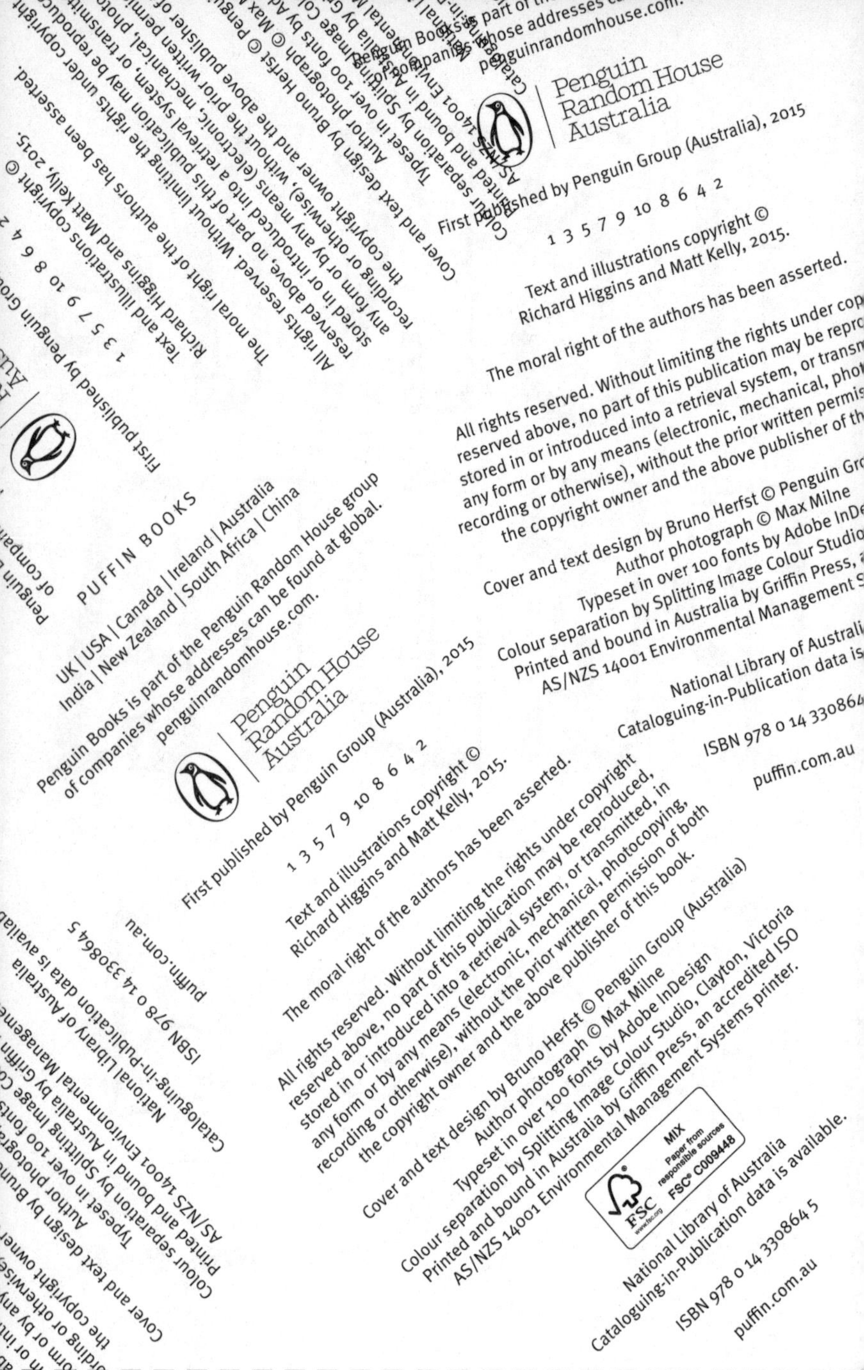

PUFFIN BOOKS

UK | USA | Canada | Ireland | Australia
India | New Zealand | South Africa | China

Penguin Books is part of the Penguin Random House group of companies whose addresses can be found at global.penguinrandomhouse.com.

Penguin Random House Australia

First published by Penguin Group (Australia), 2015

1 3 5 7 9 10 8 6 4 2

Cover and text design by Bruno Herfst © Penguin Group (Australia)
Author photograph © Max Milne
Typeset in over 100 fonts by Adobe InDesign
Colour separation by Splitting Image Colour Studio, Clayton, Victoria
Printed and bound in Australia by Griffin Press, an accredited ISO AS/NZS 14001 Environmental Management Systems printer.

MIX
Paper from responsible sources
FSC® C009448

National Library of Australia Cataloguing-in-Publication data is available.

ISBN 978 0 14 330864 5

puffin.com.au

No numbers were harmed in the writing of this book.

For Lynne Ellis,
who taught us
how to be this
disgusting.

To all the numbers. We can always count on you. Even the odd ones.

WARNING

Rated S for Stupid

G.R.O.S.S.

Government Registry of Offendedness at Stupid Stories

Dear Reader,

It is our duty to inform you that this book is filled with many disgusting words, written by two disgusting idiots who call themselves 'The Listies'. Honestly! Can you think of a worse topic for a book? We can't.

It's a book so gross that it would make a tapeworm spew. It's a book so horrible that it would make a maggot faint. That's how abominable, terrible, noxious and beastly it is. We advise you not to read it. Seriously. Stop now.

Are you still reading? Well then, what if we told you that it contains such puerile and stupid words as SPEWTIFUL, BOOGERLICIOUS and ASSMA? This is not what letters, words or punctuation were invented for.

We at G.R.O.S.S. declare that this odious publication is totally unsuitable for babies, children, tweens, teens and old people everywhere.

Yours offendedly,

Frank Lee Outraged,
Fudd E. Duddy,
& A. Noid.

G.R.O.S.S Inspectors, Canberra.

DO NOT READ ON!

WARNING. WARNING. Too much reading may cause COUNTSTIPATION.

Tips and troubleshooting for reading ICKYPEDIA:

I. Read with your eyes open.
2. Do not use a banana, wet tea bags or snot as a bookmark.
3. If the book looks like it is written in another language, try turning it I80 degrees. You could be reading it upside down.
4. If something is written in capital letters — like this: ZALKING — then it means it has its own entry in the ICKYPEDIA and you can flip through and find the definition.
5. All new words are written in RALPHABETICAL order to make them easy to find.
6. Even if you find this book too disgusting, do not place in the dishwasher.

Hello!

We are Rich and Matt, and together we are The Listies.

Welcome to ICKYPEDIA, the best book we have ever written.*

Inside these pages you will find a long list of new words that most dictionaries and encyclopedias are too afraid to print, a bunch of facts that have remained unknown for too long and heaps of never-before-seen drawings.

You are about to read the most informative, amazing and educationally important work of literature ever produced. Before its creation you would not have been able to dare your best friend to DROP PLOP off Mt Everest, you could not have warned your sister about your parents PSYCHOPASHING in the kitchen, and you would never have celebrated your HALFDAY.

So please – sit down on your REARING AID, pick a BOOGERLICIOUS booger, wipe away your EYESNOT and enjoy.

From The Listies

*Actually it's the only book we've ever written...

A is for ACHOOSPEW, when you spew out your nose.

ACHOO GOO

The little bits of snot/food that come out when you sneeze with your mouth full.

ACROCAT

A cat that can do backflips and use hula hoops.

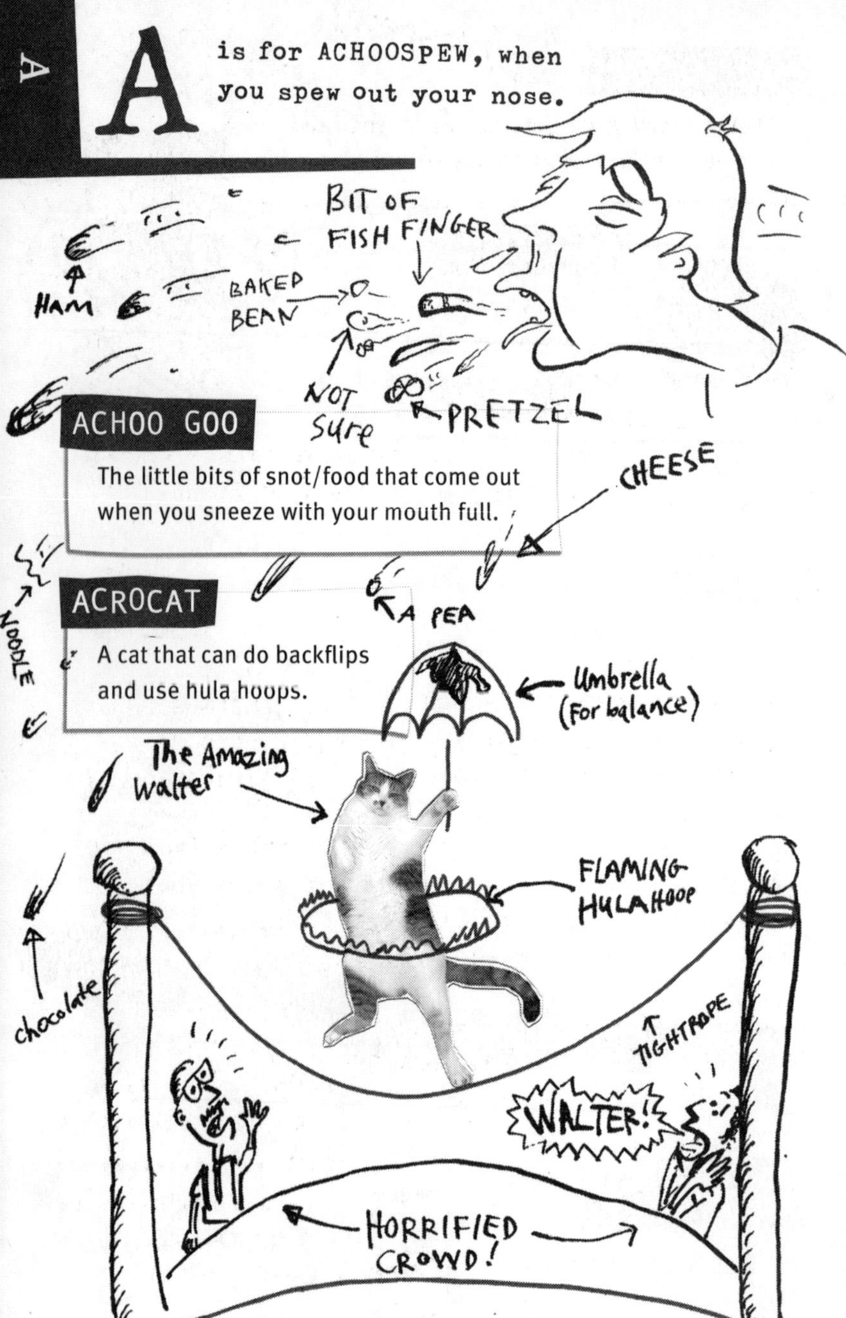

because in fact you got **2**! That's right! Included with the ICKYPEDIA

1+1=spew?

ADD NAUSEUM

That sick feeling you get when you have to add numbers up. Such as in a surprise maths quiz.

ADOORABLE

A really cute door.

ADULTSPEAK

Words adults use that no one knows the meaning of, like 'sensible', 'mortgage' and EFFING.

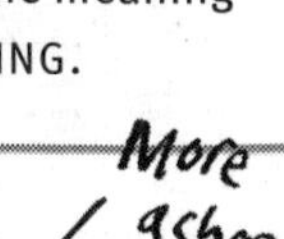

AFROZE

A wig made of ice and then sprayed with liquid nitrogen to keep it from melting. Great on hot days – it's the head equivalent of putting your undies in the freezer.

Past Blast

The first European to poo in Australia was Craptain Cook, who dropped one over the side of his ship in Bottomy Bay. It is important to realise, however, that Aboriginal people had been pooing there for 70,000 years.

AIROOMA

The gross smell of your sister's/brother's/grandparents' bedroom.

ALEXANDER GRAHAM SMELL

The first person to poo in Scotland.

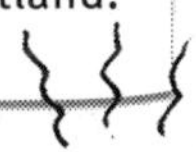

AL FLUSHCO

To go to the toilet outside.

ALLETTERGIC

An allergy to a letter of the alphabet. See also ZEALAND.

ALPHABURP

To burp the alphabet.

AMOOSING

What cows' jokes are.

ANGRY TURDS

Your toilet's fave app.

ANIMOBILES

Part animal, part mode of transport, like snail-copter: part snail, part helicopter. See also HOG AIR BALLOON.

ANNA GRAM

The woman who invented mixing up letters in one word to make a new word.

Hey Rich? Wanna hear me do an ALPHABURP?
Err. No?
But WHY?!
BECAUSE!
But WHY Because?
BECAUSE Because!
But WHY BECAUSE BECAUSE?
WHY WHY WHY WHY WHY WHY WHY WHY WHY WHY WHY WHY WHY WHY WHY WHY WHY WHY WHY WHY WHY WHY WHY WHY WHY
MATT! STOP BEING SUCH AN ASKHOLE!
...Why?
M

ARCHIPELEGO

A whole island made of Lego, rumoured to be off the coast of Denmark.

ASKHOLE

A person who asks too many questions.

ASSMA

When you breathe through your bum.

ASTRONAUGHT

An astronaut who never made it.

ASSTRONOMERS

People who specialise in the science of giant gas planets. See also BERZERKCURY, JUPITERGH and URANUS.

AVALAMBCHE

Having a lot of lambs fall on you. It can be quite inconvenient and is easily avoided by regular use of a LAMBOMETER.

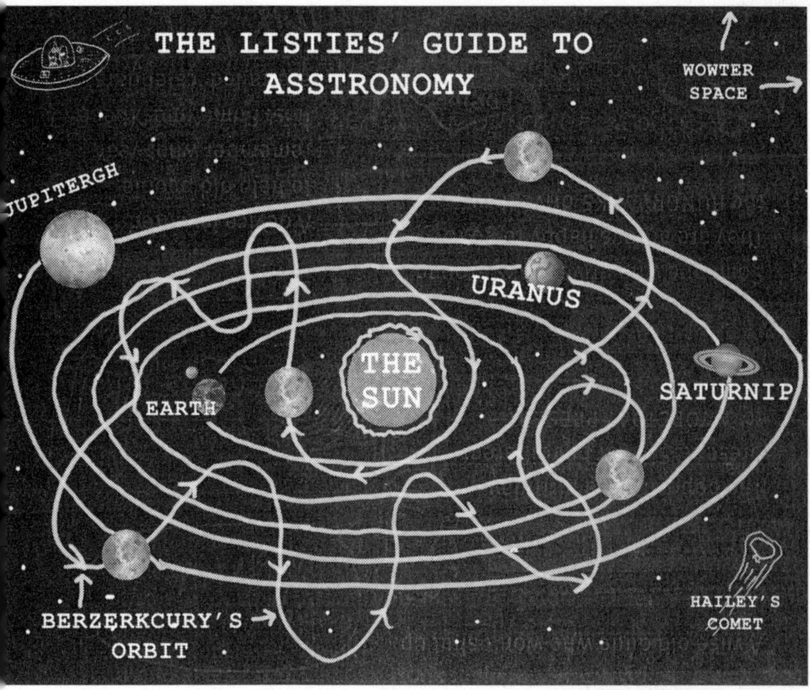

THE LISTIES' GUIDE TO ASSTRONOMY

WOWTER SPACE

JUPITERGH

URANUS

THE SUN

EARTH

SATURNIP

HAILEY'S COMET

BERZERKCURY'S ORBIT

Past Blast

THE AZTIC-TAC EMPIRE

This was an ancient culture known for having the freshest breath. They carried all their belongings around in tiny plastic containers.

AWESOON

When something awesome is going to happen really soon.

your life, have you in 7th Heaven and make you totally hungry for

B

B is for BART, when you barf and fart at the same time.

BACKPACKSTACK

When you accidentally put your school bag on upside-down and everything falls out.

BALLOONATIC

Someone who is crazy about balloons.

BANANADRAMA

When a banana has squished in your bag and everything is covered in banana goo.

BANANA SPIT

Yellow, gooey-looking phlegm on a footpath.

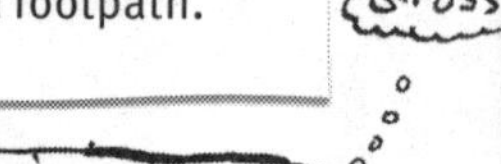

BARPING

When someone burps and farts at the same time.

The world's longest BBQUEUE

BBQUEUE

A line that forms when people are waiting for their sausages to be ready.

BEDTIME BOREY

A book you read just before bed that is so dull it's guaranteed to make you fall asleep.

Did You Know?

The most famous author of BEDTIME BOREYS is Roald Dull (not be confused with the very NOT boring stories of Roald Dahl). Roald Dull's top BEDTIME BOREYs are:

1. ***Charlie and the Carob Factory***: Ever wondered where this chocolate substitute comes from? Find out in this nine-hundred-page epic.
2. ***The BFG – The Bright Fluorescent Globes***: The story of a girl called Sophie who sensibly switches the light globes in her house to energy-saving ones.
3. ***James and the Medium Peach***: A young boy who grows a biggish peach in his front garden and then nothing else happens.
4. ***The Whiches***: An informative book that helps you work out which witch is which.

5. ***The Twitters***: The thoroughly uninteresting tale of two internet trolls. #boring

6. ***Buoy***: A collection of tales of ocean markers. You will be surprised at the stories they harbour.

7. ***Unremarkable Mr Fox***: Mr Fox gets up, eats breakfast, goes to work, comes home, watches 'Dancing with the Stars', and goes to bed. The end.

8. ***George's Prescription Medicine***: George's doctor puts him on antibiotics for his tonsillitis. He gets better.

BEEMOJI

Smiley faces and other pictures bees use to chat online.

BELCH SQUELCH

The noise at the end of a burp that indicates a bit of food has come up too.

BERZERKCURY

A planet with a crazy orbit that covers the entire solar system. Some ASSTRONOMERS think that this is, in fact, the only planet that exists, but it whizzes around the solar system so fast it looks like there are more.

BIGGISH BANG

The bang that occurred just before the one that really got the universe started.

BIN JUICE

The watery stuff at the bottom of the kitchen bin. No matter how thirsty you are, do not drink it!

BIN SIN

When someone puts recyclables in thc normal bln and vice versa.

BITNICK

Someone who nicks a bit of food off your plate.

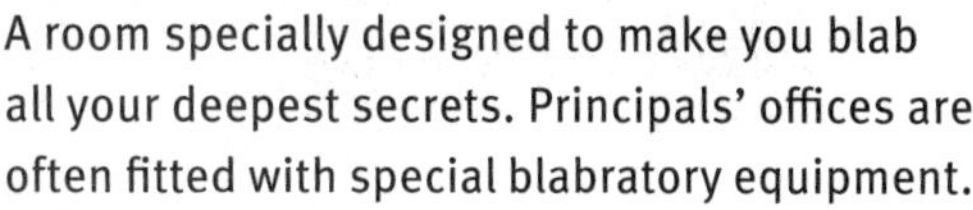

BLABRATORY

A room specially designed to make you blab all your deepest secrets. Principals' offices are often fitted with special blabratory equipment.

BLEEP

To swear in your sleep.

BLINDSIGHT

Something that seemed like a good idea at the time but turned out to be not so good, like hiding a chocolate bar in your underpants.

BLING BLING

The noise an expensive phone makes.

BLISTORY

The historical study of blisters.

BLUNDERBUTT

A bum that goes off accidentally.

BOILER ALERT

To warn someone just before you squeeze a juicy boil or pimple.

BOOGERLICIOUS

A tasty piece of snot.

Did You Know?

The first blisters in history occurred in Greco-Roman times when everyone in the fashion-conscious city of Blisterspopalot invented sandals before they invented socks. The resulting blisters on people's feet were so painful that they could only walk a few steps without having to sit down and get a foot spa. The problem was solved when philosopher Archofthefootemedes invented socks while in the bath. [He was having a wash because someone had yelled YOUREEKA at him.]

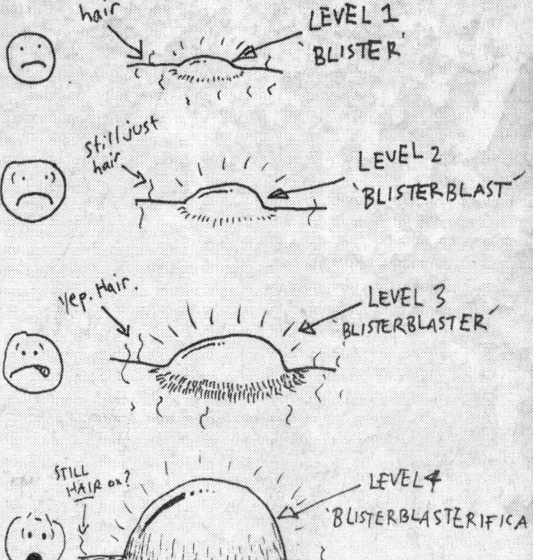

BOOKERS

What your book gets covered in when you sneeze on it.

BOTTOM BURP

A fart that smells so much of undigested food it could easily be mistaken for a burp. Opposite of MOUTH FART.

BOW-VOW

What dogs say on their wedding day.

BRAG QUEEN

Someone who's always telling you about the amazing things they've been up to.

BRAT-WORST

A really bad sausage.

Ingredients: BLU-TACK

Method: **1**. MOULD BLU-TACK INTO THE SHAPE OF A SAUSAGE.

2. EAT.

THE COLD DOG

Ingredients: 1 HOT DOG FRANKFURT
1 PADDLE POP STICK

HOT DOG (FROZEN)

PADDLE POP STICK

Method: **1**. INSERT PADDLE POP STICK INTO THE BOTTOM OF THE FRANKFURT (THE BOTTOM END IS THE ONE WITH THE LEAST AMOUNT OF RED SKIN).

2. PLACE IN FREEZER OVERNIGHT.

3. TAKE OUT AND EAT LIKE AN ICY-POLE. BE CAREFUL NOT TO EAT TOO QUICKLY AS YOU COULD GET A BRAIN FREEZE.

CARPET

CARPET SALAMI

Ingredients:

ROLL OF MASKING TAPE

A LARGE AREA OF CARPET

Method:

1. USE MASKING TAPE TO PICK UP BITS OF FLUFF, DIRT AND OTHER YUCK STUFF FROM THE CARPET. DIFFERENT PEOPLE PREFER CARPET SALAMI FROM DIFFERENT AREAS AROUND THE HOUSE. SOME PEOPLE ARE LOUNGE-ROOM CARPET SALAMI PEOPLE, SOME ARE BEDROOM CARPET SALAMI PEOPLE. WE ARE HALLWAY CARPET SALAMI PEOPLE, AS HALLWAYS TEND TO BE VACUUMED LESS AND THE STUFF YOU FIND THERE IS OF A BETTER VINTAGE.
2. IF TAPE HAS ANY REMAINING STICK, USE IT TO ROLL INTO A LONG, ROUND SHAPE.
3. PLACE IN MICROWAVE FOR 80 MINUTES ON HIGH.
4. SERVE WITH KIMCHI.

THE SCHOOL-BAG SNAG

The School-Bag Snag takes a while to make but remember: gross things come to those who wait.

Ingredients: 1 SCHOOL BAG

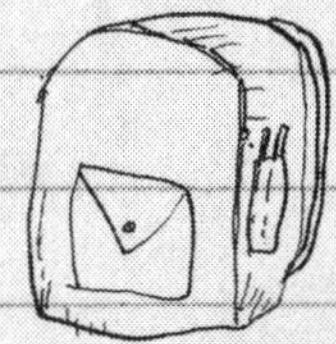

SCHOOL LUNCH OR LUNCHES

CHOCOLATE MILK

1 SPRIG PARSLEY

(GARNISH ONLY)

chocolate milk

Method:

1. TAKE LUNCH TO SCHOOL EVERY DAY FOR A COUPLE OF WEEKS/MONTHS/YEARS.

2. DO NOT EACH LUNCH. ALLOW UNEATEN FOOD TO PILE UP IN THE BOTTOM OF YOUR SCHOOL BAG ALONG WITH PENCIL SHAVINGS, SPORTS SOCKS, USED TISSUES AND MATHS HOMEWORK. IF YOU GET HUNGRY, TELL YOUR BEST FRIEND THAT YOU ARE MAKING THE SCHOOL-BAG SNAG AND ARE HAPPY TO SHARE IT WITH THEM IF

THEY SHARE THEIR LUNCH WITH YOU FOR THE NEXT FEW WEEKS/MONTHS/YEARS. THERE IS NO WAY THEY WILL REFUSE.

CHOCO-LATE MILK

3. EVERY COUPLE OF DAYS POUR IN A FEW TABLESPOONS OF CHOCOLATE MILK. YOU CAN USE STRAWBERRY OR VANILLA MILK IF YOU PREFER.

4. CHECK THE DECISMELL LEVEL OF THE SCHOOL BAG. ONCE IT IS GOOD AND SOUR ZIP THE BAG UP TIGHT.

5. TIGHTEN THE SCHOOL BAG'S STRAPS AROUND THE OUTSIDE TO MAKE A SAUSAGE-ISH SHAPE.

6. PLACE IN BOOT OF CAR.

7. THE MOMENT SOMEONE DISCOVERS THE SCHOOL-BAG SNAG IT'S READY TO EAT.

8. GARNISH WITH PARSLEY AND MUNCH AWAY.

Typical facial expression of a person who just found a school bag snag...

BRILLINQUENT

Someone who is very good at being bad.
See also THE FARTFUL DODGER.

BROWPOPPER

The vein that appears on a teacher's face when they are really angry.

BUBBLEBATTLE

A bubblegum bubble-blowing competition.

BUBBLEBATTLE

COBRA VS CAMEL

MATHEMATIC-TACS to break the curse. They packed up of their favourite kinds of sweets and trekked to

Did You Know?

The biggest bubblegum bubble ever blown was 540 000 000 km wide and was blown by a young girl called Halley Chew. Her bubble was so big it blocked out the sun, forcing NASA to blast it into space. You can see it when it orbits the earth every 76.5 years. ASSTRONOMERS have named it Halley's comet.

BUDGIE SMUGGLERS

A tight-fitting pair of DAD SAGS.

Did You Know?

Budgie smugglers were originally developed by pirates to smuggle budgies, parrots and birds of prey in and out of Australia. The pirates didn't use them because injuries were too common. Australia's fondness for this piece of clothing is celebrated in a roadside statue. See also ENBIGENATE.

BUFFER SUFFER

That agonising amount of time when you're waiting for a YouTube clip to load.

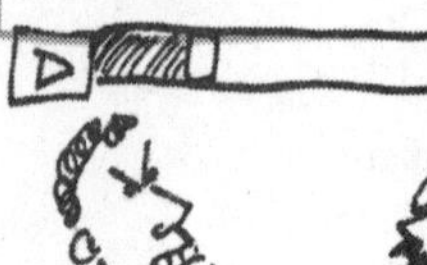

The face of a pirate trying to smuggle budgies in his BUDGIE SMUGGLERS

BUMOUR

A bum tumour. An unexplained lump on your bum.

1. 2.

Mum! It's happened again!

BUMPDUMP

When your mum or dad goes over a speed bump so fast you accidentally poo.

BURLK

To burp while talking.

BURPRA SINGER

Someone who can sing and burp at the same time.

Past Blast

BUM TZU

Bum Tzu was an ancient Chinese warrior who wrote the infamous military strategy book The Fart of War. It included the infamous technique of loading up on spicy Szechuan food, dim sum and wombok (chinese cabbage) the day before a battle and making sure the enemy was downwind. Famous quotes attributed to Bum Tzu are: 'All warfare is based on digestion' and 'She will win who knows when to fart and when not to fart'.

THE FART OF WAR

Past Blast

BYZANTINY EMPIRE, THE

The Byzantiny Empire was the smallest empire in history. Famed for exporting carpets which people used for dolls' houses, the Byzantiny markets were called 'bizarres' because it was weird how small they were. The Byzantiny Empire was taken over by the Emperor Constantiny in 306 CE (Compact Era) and renamed Constantiny. It is now known as Istansmall, a city so miniscule you can't see it on a map no matter how hard you look.

* ← The Emperor Constantiny (Actual size)

Istansmall →

The whole of the Byzantiny Empire →

17 Types of Burps

The Listies

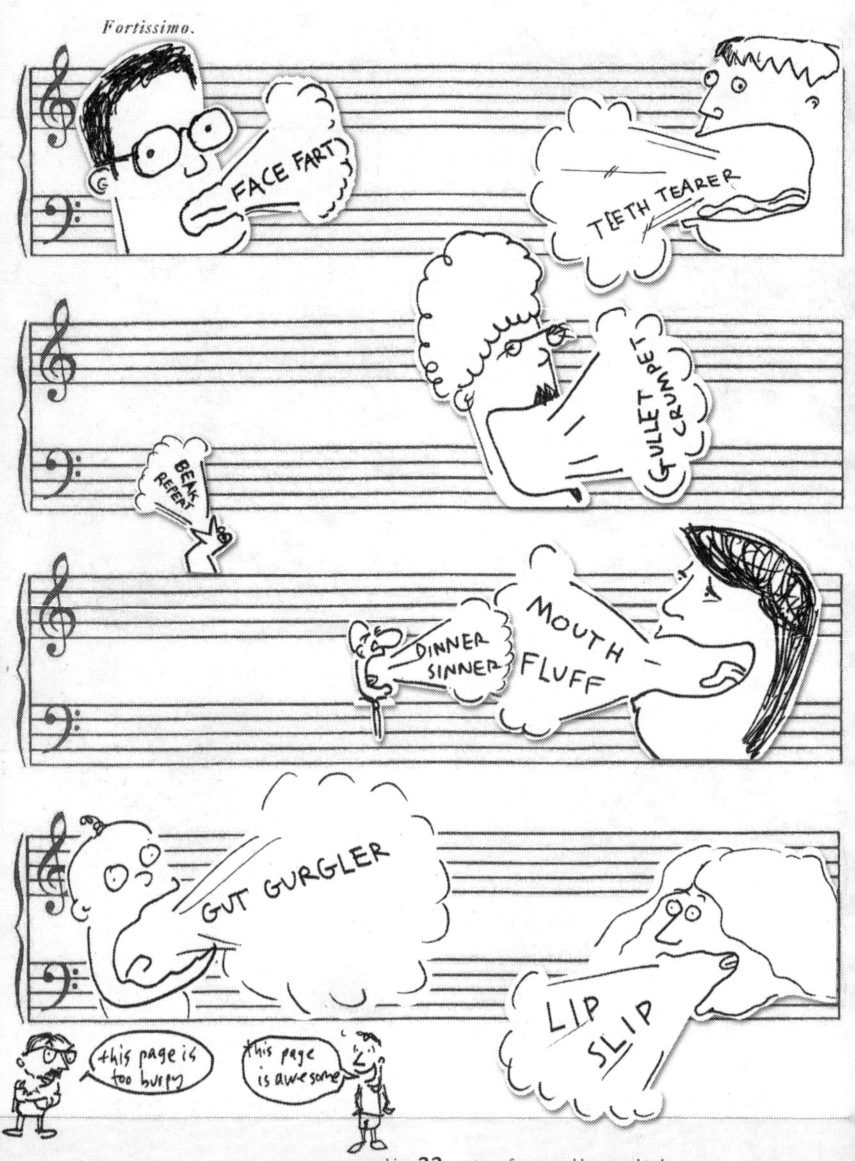

was covered in **22** metres of snow and happened to be

the home of of the world's smartest species of yak. These yaks were

C is for CHUNDER FROM DOWN UNDER, which is part vomit, part diarrhoea.

Did You Know?

The world's first carpark was designed by Miss Sue Bishi. It was a large flat concrete area with no swings, slides, monkey bars or grass. As a park it was really dull. People who went there were so bored they went to the shopping centre across the road, leaving their cars behind. And thus the carpark was born. They are now very popular and can be seen all over the world, except in the sea.

CARBUMKLE

A pimple on your bum. It may develop into a BUMOUR.

CAREOKE

Singing in the car.

CARPARKSHARK

Someone who stalks unsuspecting families in crowded carparks in order to snaffle up their park.

CAR PET

A pet that lives in your car.

CAST OFF!

When you take off a plaster cast that's been on for ages and it smells totally off.

CHANCERS

Answers you give on the off-chance they might be right.

CHATTER SPLATTER

A bit of food that comes flying out of your mouth as you speak.

CHEEKFREAK

An aunty/uncle/random friend of your parents who always wants to kiss you hello on the cheek.

CHEESETAH

A spotty cheese that runs away really fast when you try to eat it.

CHOPTOBER

To eat using only chopsticks for a whole month.

CHUCKNOLOGY

Technology that helps you throw things, e.g. catapults and slingshots.

CHUCK NORRIS

The guy who invented spewing.

Hurrrl!

CLICKWIT

Someone who learns everything from the internet.

CLOCKBLOCKER

Someone who refuses to tell you the time even though they are wearing a watch.

CLUCKOPATRA

The queen of chickens. See also EGGYPT.

COCK-A-DOODLE POO

The morning's first poo.

OTHER CODES INCLUDE:

HYPERCOLOUR	When you are about to **KANGASPEW** or are on the eve of a **SPEWPOCOLYPSE**.
YELLOW	When you say **HALLOWEE**, find something **SCAREWEE** or need an **R.I.PEE**.
GREEN	When you have a **DANGLE BOOGER**, a **TISSUE ISSUE** or are dancing the **HANKYFANDANGO**.
BEIGE	When you are reading a **BEDTIME BOREY**, eating from a **SMORGASBORED** or watching a movie starring Yawn Cruise.
RAINBOW	All of the above.

CODE BROWN

What you yell when you need to do an emergency number two.

COMPOISTURE

The runny watery stuff at the bottom of the compost bucket. Like BIN JUICE but more organic.

COMPOSTER IMPOSTER

Something in the compost bin that doesn't belong there.

CONGEALIES

What is left in the sink after you* have washed up.

(*By 'you' we mean your mum or dad.)

COPYCAT

To photocopy a cat.

COUNTSTIPATED

When you get stuck counting.

CRAPAPPLE

A really disgusting apple.

this can happen when you read this book

CRAUGHING

Crying and laughing at the same time.

CROSSANTS

Really angry bread products.

CRYDEA

To have an idea while crying.

CZECH MATE

A friend made in Prague.

and the order, putting it right before and the curse was lifted. True story, though we did

D

D is for DOCTOR SHOCKER, when you spew on a doctor.

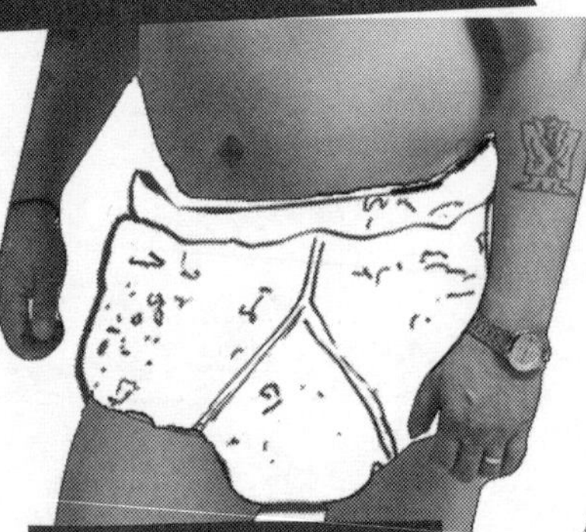

DAD SAGS

Saggy swimming trunks that have lost their elastic and are really embarrassing. See also WHY-FRONTS?

DANGLE BOOGER

Snot that gets caught in old people's nose hair.

DA VINCI TOAD

Not many people realise that artist Leonardo da Vinci had a very talented pet toad. It was actually responsible for most of his more inventions and paintings. It was also in charge of keeping the fly population in the studio down.

DECAYMAN ISLANDS

Really disgusting islands made entirely of mulch, compost and dead bodies. A popular holiday resort for zombies. See also RUBBISHAREA.

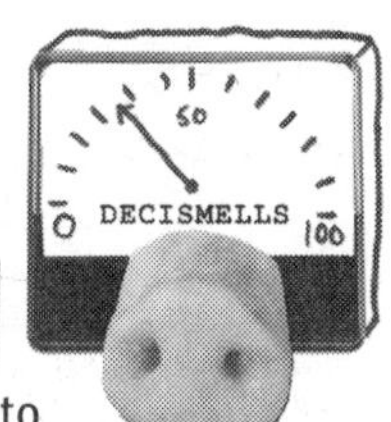

DECISMELL

The scale used to measure how much something stinks.

DESTRUCTIONS

Instructions you should never follow. (Don't do this at home. Don't do this at school. Don't do this anywhere. Ever.)

How Not to Have a Haircut

RED CORDIAL + + =

DIAHEAR

To hear someone pooing.

This guy can hear someone pooing

DIABOLICK

To lick something disgusting, like EYESNOT, BIN JUICE, or CONGEALIES. Possibly as a dare in order to receive YUCK BUCKS.

DIGISNOZZLED

Getting your finger stuck up your nose.

DINOSORE

The biggest blister you have ever seen.

DIRTY LAWNDRY

A front yard that desperately needs someone to pick up the dog poo.

DISGUSTATION

When everything on the menu is horrible.

DONOT

An extremely useful word that can be used to describe everything in the world that is not a donut.

DOWNFARTED

The sad feeling you get when you think you're going to do an OZONESLAYER, but it turns out to be a FLEAFART.

DRIP SNIFF

When you stop snot from falling out your nose by sniffing.

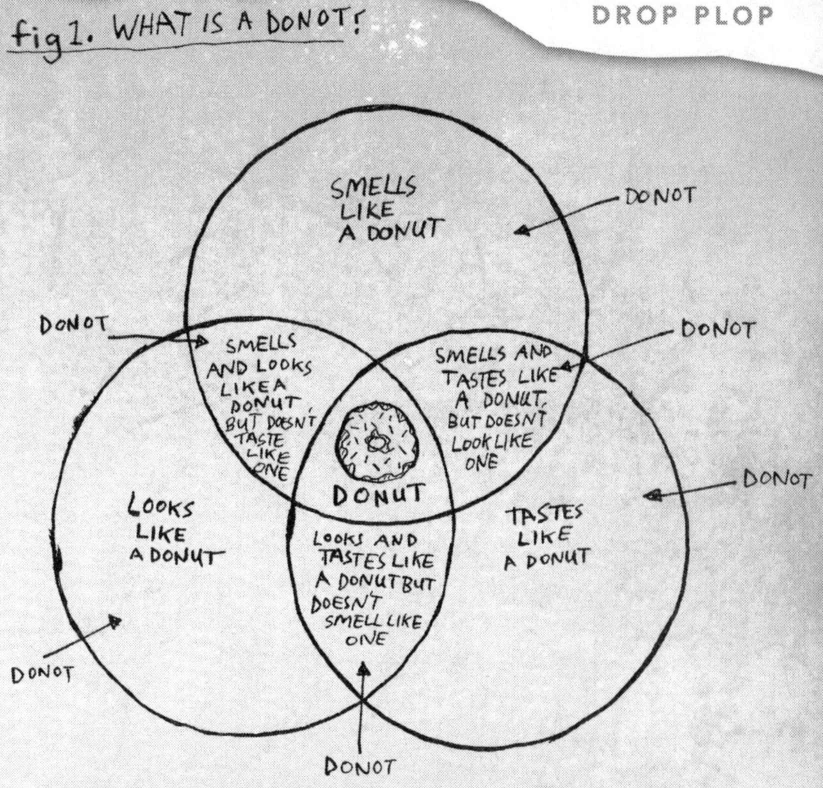

fig 1. WHAT IS A DONOT?

SMELLS LIKE A DONUT

LOOKS LIKE A DONUT

TASTES LIKE A DONUT

SMELLS AND LOOKS LIKE A DONUT, BUT DOESN'T TASTE LIKE ONE

SMELLS AND TASTES LIKE A DONUT, BUT DOESN'T LOOK LIKE ONE

LOOKS AND TASTES LIKE A DONUT BUT DOESN'T SMELL LIKE ONE

DONUT

DONOT

DONOT

DONOT

DONOT

DONOT

DONOT

DROP PLOP

To poo from a great height, like into a long-drop toilet, into the Grand Canyon, or out of a helicopter.

E

E for ETCH-A-RETCH, when you throw up in a line-shape pattern.

EARSPEW

When there is so much wax coming out of someone's ears it's like they're spewing.

EARTHWORM-HOLES

Contrary to popular opinion, dolphins are not the most intelligent animal – earthworms are. Worm physicists have recently discovered earthworm-holes, rents in the time space continuum that allow worms to teleport anywhere without travelling through the ground. This is how worms turn up mysteriously on footpaths, in indoor pot plants and in people's poos.

EARTING

To eat with your ears.

EASTER PEGS

In the olden days the Easter bunny used to bring wooden clothes pegs, called Easter pegs, and hide them underneath the washing line for children to hunt. It was the lamest holiday of the year, and so many people signed online petitions that the Easter bunny people were contacted and they changed it to chocolate eggs because everyone likes chocolate.

EDITH DEFECOWAN

The first woman to be elected to the Australian Parliament, and poo there, was Edith Defecowan in 1921. The first female Prime Minister to use the loo in the PM's office was Poolia Gillard.

EENK

A knee that can bend backwards. See also WOBLE.

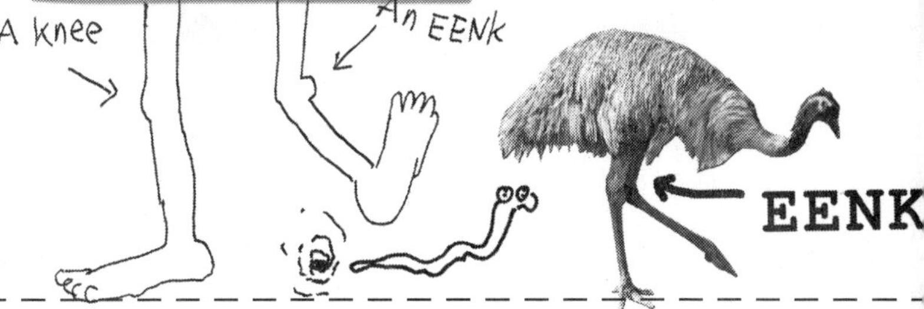

EFFING

A word in ADULTSPEAK that roughly translates as 'really' i.e. 'The way that person has parked is EFFING annoying!' or 'Stop swearing, it's EFFING rude!'

MATT LEARNS A NEW WORD.

if you answer correctly you will get **37** points added to your score. It's quite simple.

Okay, let's start at question **38**, because you are really smart. Ready?

EGGMODE

The state you have entered into when all your butt burps smell like rotten eggs.

EGGSPRESS

When a chicken lays an egg really fast.

EGGSPRESSO

When an Italian chicken lays an egg really fast.

EGGSPRESSOHNO!

When an Italian chicken lays an egg really fast and it smashes.

EGGYPT

A favourite holiday destination for chickens; holds the tomb of CLUCKOPATRA.

E-GULL

A sea bird who uses technology. They just love computer chips.

EKIDNA

A spiky Australian animal who is always telling jokes.

ELBOW PIT

The inside of your elbow. See also KNEEPIT.

ELEPHANTOM

A really big ghost.

ELVIS PEASLEY

The world's most famous vegetable.

EMISSION IMPOSSIBLE

A really awesome action film about a CIA agent trying to go to the toilet but the twist is – nothing comes out! It's really suspenseful.

EMOSOCIAL

When you feel feelings in public.

ENBIGENATE

To make something big and put it by the side of the road.

ENCYCLOPEDIUMMM?

A big book of questions to which there are no answers. For example: Do man-eating sharks eat women too? Why do you have to read the card before you open the present? Why do you say goats but not sheeps? What is the sound of one lip kissing? Why don't buses go through the drive-through? How do TV people get their teeth so white? If a bear poops in the woods and no one is around, does it still smell?

Did You Know?

Australians like to celebrate things by ENBIGENATING them. There's The Big Galah in Kimba, South Australia; The Big Pineapple on the Sunshine Coast in Queensland; and even The Big Poo in Kiama, New South Wales. The first enbigenated thing was The Big Light Bulb in Gunnedah, New South Wales. However, when the people of Gunnedah turned it on they found that it was far too bright and couldn't be turned off. After a long town meeting they decided that the only thing they could do was to shoot it into space. We now call it the Sun, after its inventor Thomas Edisun.

ENJOYCE

The happiest woman in the world is called ENJOYCE. She's actually pretty annoying.

CHEEEEEEEEEEESE!

ENORGEOUS
When something is big and beautiful.

EPHLEGMERA
When you spit on the pavement and it fades away.

EQUESTION
A horse that asks too many questions. See also ASKHOLE.

E-QUIP
A witty message sent via email.

ESCARGO
The things snails carry in their shells.

E-SNAIL
Someone who takes ages to answer emails.

wake it up. Next question: Name a number larger than **42**. Think carefully. Got it?

EWWWTUBE

The internet's most disgusting site. Don't even think about googling it.

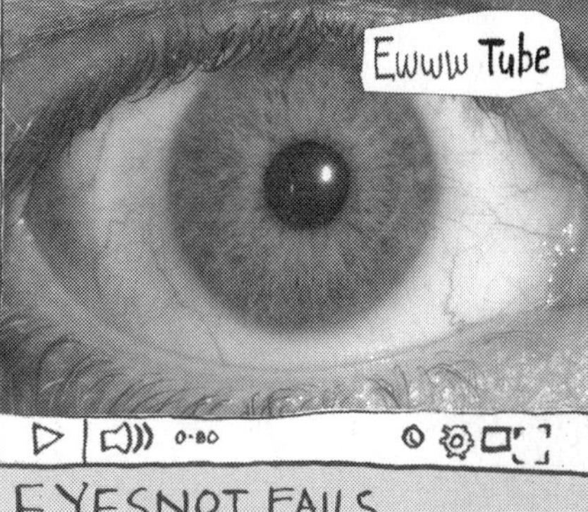

EXORCYST

Someone who squeezes other people's zits.

EXPLOSEAN

The person who invented explosions. What an awesome guy.

EXQUIZZARDS

Good-looking guts.

EYESNOT

When the goop coming out of your eyes is actually snot. Possibly one of the grossest things in ICKYPEDIA.

is for FACE OFF, when you throw up so hard your face comes off.

FACEPOOP

A social network for poos.

FAAAAARRRRRRTTTTT

When a bum burp goes on longer than expected.

FAIL — EPIC FAIL — GLOBAL FAIL — GALAXY FAIL — INFINITY FAIL

FAIL SCALE

A scale used to measure how badly something went wrong.

FAILIENS

The most hopeless species in the universe. They have attempted to invade earth millions of times and never succeeded.

FAIRY FAILS

Once-upon-a-time stories where characters don't live happily ever after.

FANGGANG

A group of vampires.

FANGRY

When a vampire gets hangry (hungry and angry).

FARTFUL DODGER, THE

Someone who always blames others for their own stinky-bum crimes.

FARTLE

When a fart startles you.

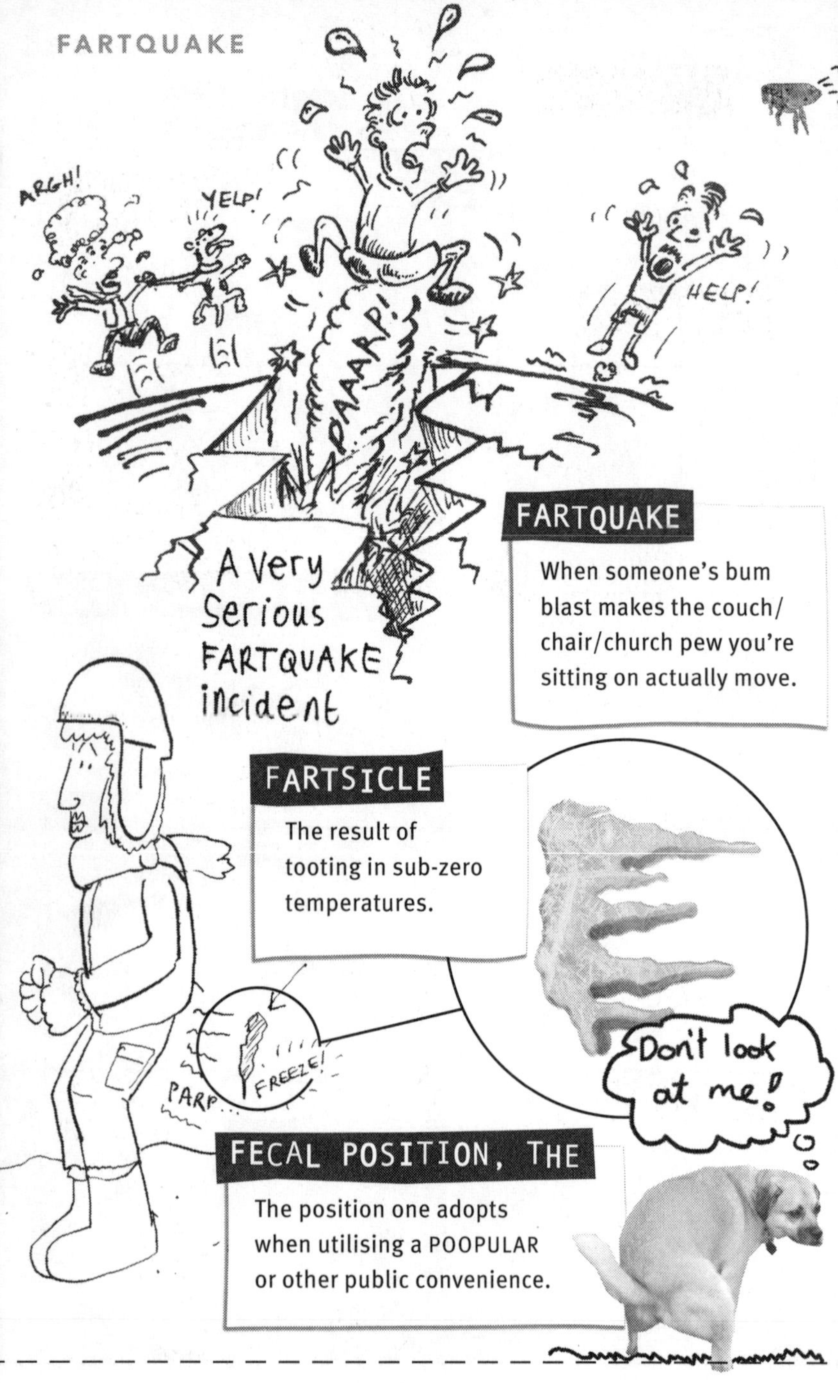

FARTQUAKE

When someone's bum blast makes the couch/chair/church pew you're sitting on actually move.

FARTSICLE

The result of tooting in sub-zero temperatures.

FECAL POSITION, THE

The position one adopts when utilising a POOPULAR or other public convenience.

FIBBACIST

A professional liar. Fibbacists often have quite a high LIE-Q.

FINDCRAFT

A time-consuming game you play with yourself based on wandering around your room trying to find something you've lost.

FISHCORD

The long thin stringy thing that sometimes hangs out of a goldfish's butt. People will try to tell you that this is the way fish do their toilet business, but actually if the FISHCORD is pulled the fish will instantly inflate to ten times its normal size.

FLEAFART

A very quiet fart.

FLICK FLOP

A deadly weapon often used as the finishing move in the Australian martial arts style called THONG-DO. See also NANJITSU.

You're doing really great! Let's skip ahead to level **47**, okay? Right then,

FLIERRHEA

A sloppy bird poo.

FLOPERA SINGING

Singing really badly and really loudly.

FLOPERATION

When an operation goes disastrously wrong.

Guys..... has anyone seen my watch?

or my shoes?

or my keys?

or my golf clubs?

or my phone?

or my phone charger?

Or the remote control?

Or my cat ?

FLOP FLIP

When you put your foot thongs on the wrong way round.

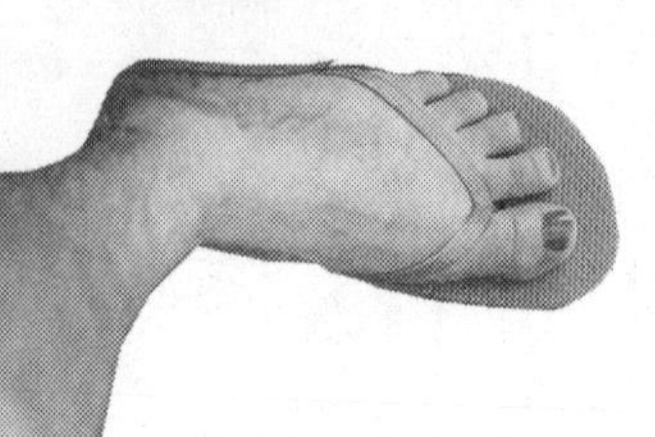

FLOSSICKING

Trying to dig a bit of food out of your teeth using something you shouldn't. Mums and dads can often been seen using folded-up pieces of paper, earrings and car keys.

FLUFFOLOGIST

An expert on fluff. See also FUZZLETRUMPLE.

FLYRIS

A bug that lands in your eye and tries to live there.

FOOL SCHOOL

When someone is trying to teach you something that you know isn't true, they are taking you to fool school. Fool schools were first opened by famous FIBBACIST Sir Liessac Spewton.

FRANKEN SAUSAGE

A sausage that has been left on the BBQ for too long.

FRENCH FLIES

The crispy zapped flies that pile up in the bottom of a bug zapper. They taste excellent with tomato sauce. Dutch people eat their French flies with mayonnaise.

FRIDGETARIAN

A person who refrigerates things unnecessarily.

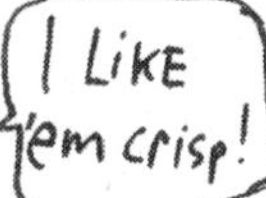

FRUDIST

A piece of fruit you don't have to peel before eating, like apples, pears, grapes and tomatoes. A collection of more than three of these in a bowl is called a FRUDIST colony.

FRUIN

To ruin a wholesome, perfectly unhealthy snack by adding fruit to it.

FUDDY DADDY

A dad who has trouble keeping up with technology.

FUNION

A really funny onion.

FUNTASY

To daydream of doing something more fun.

FURNATURE

Indoor furniture that has been left outside for too long and has gone feral, like a couch that has been dumped next to the shed and gets full of spiders.

FUZZLETRUMPLE

A friendly life-form that can evolve in the belly button if the fluff is never cleaned out.

CAN I EAT THIS?

the number 53? Then from that number

G

G is for GREAT SPLATSBY, the world's best vomiter. Winner of three green medals at The Vomitwealth Games.

GAME DRAIN

To use all the battery on your phone/tablet playing games.

What GANGREEN Looks Like in black and white....

GANGREEN

The most awesomely icky of all of the colours.

GARBAGGAGE

To pack all your trash into a suitcase and send it overseas.

GARGOLOYAL

An ugly statue that will never let you down.

HAPPY HALFDAY MATT

GAS SASS

To burp in someone's face. Rude, but sometimes unavoidable.

GAZELLEN

The most famous talk show host on the African savannah.

GENIAINT

Someone who thinks they are a genius but they ain't.

GERMINATOR

What you turn into when you're cleaning up.

GET ONE'S GHOST

To really annoy a supernatural being.

GHOULIE

The scariest position in soccer.

GIDDY-UP CHUCK

A vomit performed on a horse.

GIGANTICK

The mark made next to an answer that is really, really correct.

GINJURY

To hurt the feelings of a person with red hair.

GNATURAL

Natural for gnats.

GIRAFFLE

A competition you enter where the main prize is a giraffe.

1st PRIZE

GLEEK

A vegetable that knows heaps about computers.

GOB SLOB

A person who always misses their mouth when eating. Babies are terrible gob slobs.

GOLIARTH

The name given to someone who is a gigantic liar.

GOOGLESNOOZE

To forget something as soon as you've finished googling it.

GOSSLIP

To accidentally tell someone something you shouldn't.

GRAFEETI

To spray-paint your feet.

GRAFIGHT

To argue over a pencil.

GRANWICH

A gran sandwich.

Past Blast

GREAT DEPRESSION, THE

During The Great Depression people were so poor they couldn't even afford toilet paper. So after going to the loo, they dragged themselves along the nature strips like dogs do. This is the origin of the phrase, 'the grass is always greener on the other side', because the other side of the street always looked less brown.

GREAT BARRIER TEETH

The furry coral-like stuff that grows on your teeth when you don't brush them. See also HALITO-SHUSH.

GRINGAP

The gap in your smile where a tooth once was.

GRINCANYON

When you have two GRINGAPS in a row.

GROSSBOAST

To proudly show off a blister/pimple/bruise/wart etc.

GROSSTASTIC

When something is fantastically gross.

GRUMPAS

Grandpas who aren't happy; crazy grandpas.

GUMCHUMS

Little bits of food that get caught between your teeth.

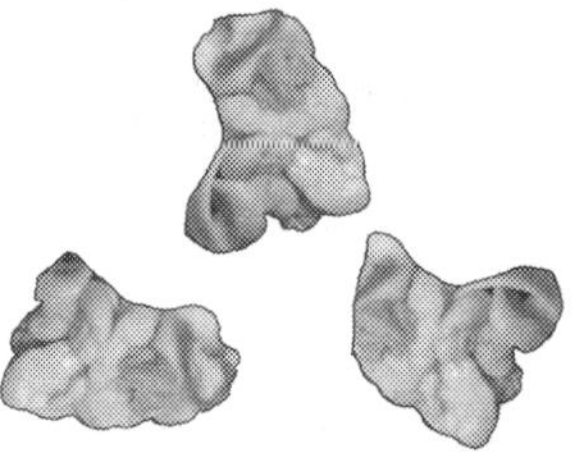

GUMNUT

Someone who never throws out their chewing gum. See also BUBBLEBATTLE.

GUMMY BARES

Naked lollies. Rude, but delicious.

GUNKET

A tiny bit of gunk.

The world's smallest GUNKET

Apart from this one

And this one

And that one

And this one

H

is for HURLICOPTER, when you spew out of a helicopter.

HAIRCROW

To make a human-sized doll from the hair found in the shower plug. Useful for scaring people away from the bathroom so you can have some privacy in there.

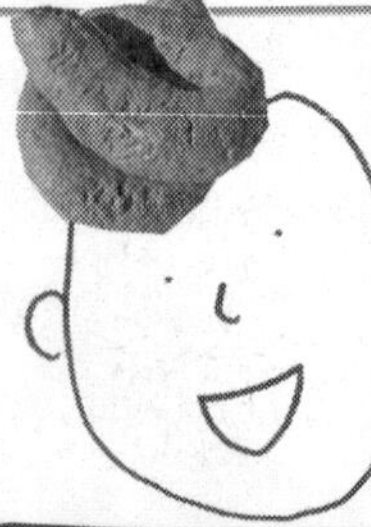

HAIRDO-DO

To improvise hair product with animal dung. This can be a very effective, if slightly smelly, solution to a HAIRUM SCARUM; however, be warned, it may make it worse.

HAIRUM SCARUM

A haircut so bad it's terrifying.

HAIRYFLOSS

The weird hair that grows on your dad's toes and feet (also happens to mums).

HALFDAY

The day you celebrate your ½ birthday. This happens exactly halfway between your last birthday and your next. To celebrate it properly insist your parents give you a half card, sing you half the birthday song and let you eat a whole piece of cake – it is your halfday after all!

HALITO-SHUSH

When you can't tell someone that they have bad breath. See also GREAT BARRIER TEETH.

HALLOWEE

A holiday where people dress up in scary costumes, knock on their neighbour's door and threaten to wee on their doorstep unless they get lollies. Much, much scarier than Halloween.

HANKYFANDANGO

The dance that takes place between a hanky and your snot when you've blown out more than it can hold.

HANKY SKANKY

A really crusty hanky.

HEYFEVER

When you can't stop saying 'hey' to things.

HIBISCUITS TREE

A flowering plant that produces the world's biscuits.

HIPSTIR

To make fun of a hipster.

HOCK THE PHLEGM DISCUS

To spit.

HOG AIR BALLOON

A hot air balloon powered by pig farts. See also ANIMOBILES.

Did You Know?

In 1873 an adventurer named Phileas Hogg declared he was going to travel around the world in 80 days flying a HOG AIR BALLOON. He set off on the journey accompanied by his trusty piggy companion named Kevin Bacon. Word travelled quickly and everywhere they went huge crowds gathered to have a picture taken with the pooting pig. In fact, so many people did selfies with the swine that it is said that you are never more than six degrees of separation from someone who was once in a picture with Kevin Bacon.

HOLDON

A car that makes you need to wee. See also Y.O.L.O.

HOLIDAZE

When you are so excited about the end of term you can't think straight.

HOLY TWEET!

What birds say when they're surprised.

HOMMOUSE

A dip made from mice.

HOOTENGRANNY

When nans have a good time.

ON TONIGHT!

A HOOTEN-GRANNY!

Tea! Bingo! Chats!
KNITTING! BAKE OFF!
DRIVING SLOWLY PRACTICE!
No grandads allowed!

HORRIBABBLE

To be so scared you can't talk properly.

HORRIBULL

An evil cow.

HORSE AND FART

To be on a carriage behind a horse and have it fart in your face.

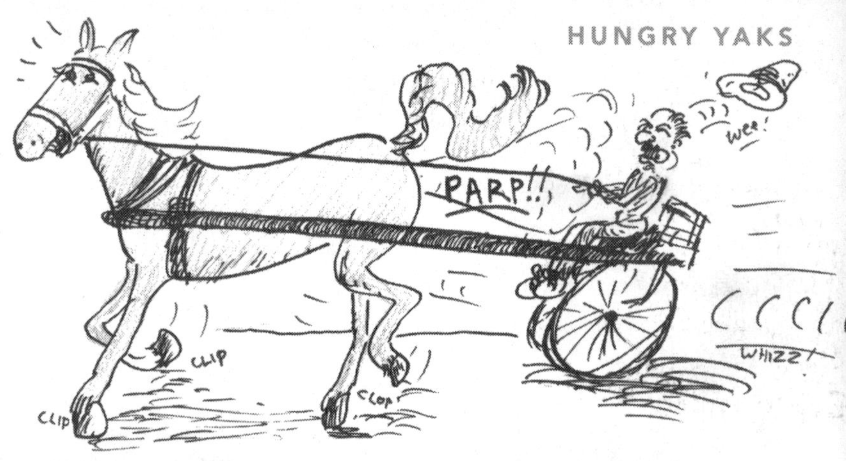

HUBBUBBLE

The excitement caused by someone blowing rare bubbles.

HUNGRY YAKS

A Himalayan fast-food franchise. An acquired taste.

DIFFERENT TYPES OF BUBBLES

This is important information to have when identifying bubbles.

- Bubble
- Doublebubble
- Triobubble
- Quadrabubble
- Pentabubble
- Hexabubble
- Heptabubble
- Octabubble
- Gigabubble
- Googlebubble
- Terrabubble
- Balloon

 years ago, who was allergic to numbers!

I

I is for iVOM, an app that can accurately predict all the times in your life you'll vomit.

ICEBURGER

A hamburger served cold and floating in a drink.

ICE-CREAM ZONE

The trance-like state your brain goes into when you're eating ice-cream.

ICE-DREAM CONE

Your ultimate ice-cream flavour combo.

IDENTIFRY

To attempt to work out what food was before it was barbequed into a charcoal lump. See also FRANKEN SAUSAGE.

IGLOO

A really cold toilet.

ICKLOO

A really disgusting toilet.

ICKSTATIC

The feeling you get when something is outstandingly icky.

ICKYPEDIA

An incredibly disgusting book you should never, ever read.

IGNORANUS

To take no notice whatsoever of your own, or anyone else's, bottom.

IGUANANA

Half iguana, half banana.

ILLEAGLE

A criminal bird. Seagulls are a fine example of these as they are always stealing chips at the beach. See also URBANNED.

IMBURPANATION

To attempt to belch like someone else.

IMPOLIGHT BULB

A rude, uncouth or inconsiderate source of light, e.g. a light that switches itself on when you're trying to sleep.

INFECTIOUS BARF

Similar to an infectious laugh, this happens if one person spews and other people hear it and can't help joining in. This phenomena can be quite SPEWTIFUL.

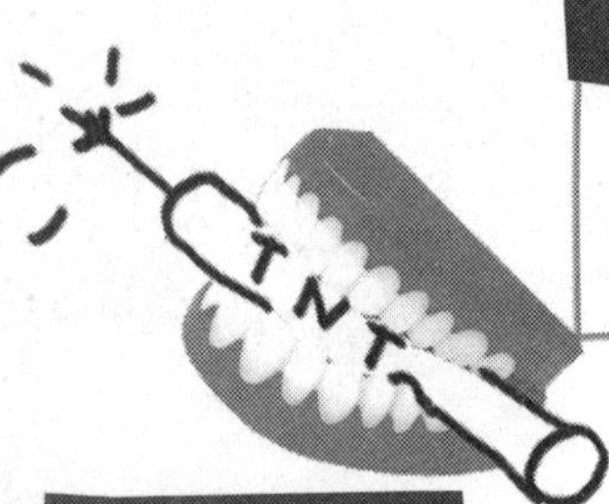

INGLISH

A language in which words are spelt exactly the way they sound. See our handy INGLISH translator on page 72.

INK RETHINK

A correction made using a ~~pencil~~ pen.

INSCISSOR

To use your teeth like scissors to cut something like sticky tape, string or the fuse wire on dynamite.

INSTALOO

Checking Instagram in the toilet. It's also a good time to update your FACEPOOP status.

INSTAGRAN

An app specifically for taking and sharing photos of grans. See also KNITTER.

This tortoise has been INTENTSIFIED.

INTENTSIFY

To really, really, really put something in a tent.

INVENTSHUNS

Great inventions no one got into.

INVISIBULL

A cow that's really hard to see. (Better hope it's not also a HORRIBULL.)

IRRITATO

A really annoying potato.

THE LISTIES' 6 MOST ~~DANGEROUS~~ EXCELLENT INVENTSHUNS

1 FIREY FLOSS

A spicy show-time snack. Enjoy this cotton candy scientifically designed to set your tastebuds alight. Literally. Breathing fire isn't just for dragons anymore.*

2 NUCLEARRINGS

Are you constantly getting teased for not having radioactive earrings? Simply grab yourself a pair of these. Best of all, they glow in the dark.**

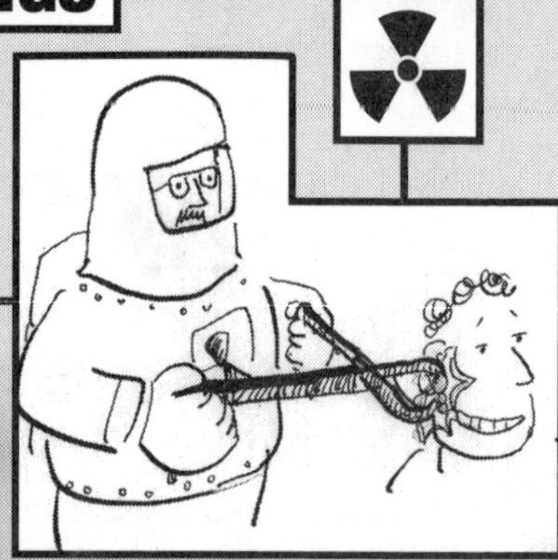

3 THE FART ALARM

Never let a good fluff go unnoticed. Strap it on, let one off, and the sound of 120-decibel sirens will announce its arrival. Works even for SBDs (silent but deadlies).***

4 **DYNAMIGHT**

Why not add the element of surprise to your explosions? Simply light the fuse and wait... it might explode, it might not. Sure to keep the whole family guessing.****

5 **BIÑATAS**

Tie on a blindfold, grab yourself a stick and take a swing at this papier-mâché party game. Instead of the typical treats of lollies and chocolates this parcel is jam-packed full of garbage swimming in a sea of BIN JUICE. Guaranteed to stink up any party. What fun! *****

6 **SLURPEAS**

SLURPEAS: What's better than an icy cold drink on a boiling hot day? Vegetables, that's what. A delicious mix of frozen peas and ice, the slurpea is soon to be the coolest drink in town.******

* Warning: Fire may result in death. ** Warning: Radioactivity will certainly lead to death. *** Warning: Volume of alarm may cause heart attack, which may then cause death. **** Warning: Explosions have resulted in death. ***** Warning: Contains bacteria that will definitely result in death. ****** Tastes a lot better than you'd think. However, if drunk too quickly this could lead to a brain freeze, which may result in death.

Inglish Tranzlaytor

Inglish	English
YOT	yacht
BLUD	blood
COF	cough
SYKICK	psychic
Q-COMEBAH	cucumber
BEECORZE	because
CORT	caught
NEWKLEAR	nuclear
WHENSDAY	wednesday
ANAMUL	animal
KOMPEWTAR	computer
XPURRT	expert
FARENDLEE	friendly
PEEPLE	people
TEECHHA	teacher
THE INNANET	the internet
DEZZERT	dessert
BAYBEE	baby
WERDS	words
PUNKSHOOAYSHON	punctuation

COSIDUNTWANNA

Because I do not want to

MUUUUMWEARZMYSKOOLCLOWZ

Mum, where are my school clothes?

JANA MEAN?

Do you know what I mean?

INGLISH IZ AY GUD LANGWIDJ. EWE KAN SPEL DE SAYME WERD MEN KNEE DEFFERANT WAIZE N THAY R AWL RITE!

FER EGGS-ARM-PULL HEAR R SIXTEEEN WHEYS TO SPEL 'ORANGE':

1 ORANJ	10 KORPHEWNGEZ [the k is silent, as are the ph, the z and the w]
2 ORAINGE	11 ( ) [in emoticon form]
3 ORAYNGE	12 ORRONGE
4 OH! RENGE	13 AWERONGE
5 HORANGE [the h is silent]	14 ORINGE
6 ARRANGE	15 OREENZJ
7 ORANJ	16 ORNG
8 AURAJNE	
9 AURENGE	

Now, this lady I mentioned about words back, who was allergic to

J is for JURASSICK PUKE, which is fossilised dinosaur barf.

"LEOPARD CHANGES HER SPOTS" by DAMIAOW! HIRST

JACOOOZIE

When someone gets into a spa with an open sore.

JAGUART

Painting by jungle cats, the most arty of all animals.

"SCRATCHING POLES" By CATSON POLLOCK (Pictured)

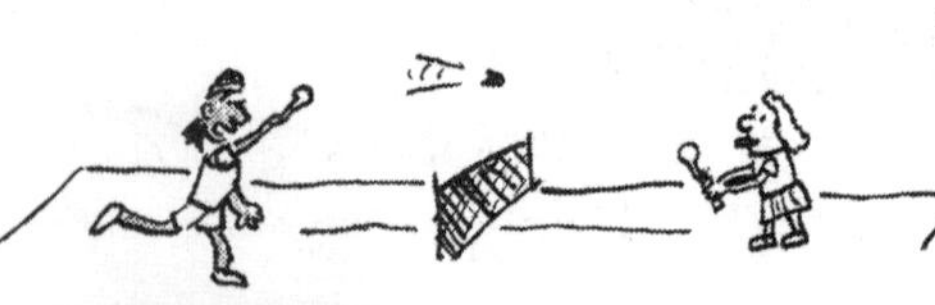

JAM SLAM

Like tennis, except players flick globs of jam at each other with spoons.

SELF PORTRAIT by LEOnardo Da Kitty

JAVELIN-IN-THE-BOX

An earlier prototype of the now common Jack-in-the-Box, the Javelin-in-the-Box was a lethal kids' toy invented by the criminally insane inventor I.M. Clearlymad. Other discontinued toys in his range were Mr Grenadey Head, Barrel o' Spiders, Play Doh'nt and the Merry-go-Drown.

JELLYOUS

The feeling you get when you really want some else's dessert.

JIFFYSTINK

A fart that doesn't stay around for very long (compared to an OZONESLAYER).

JIGSAW FIZZLE

A puzzle that has pieces missing.

JIM NASIUM

The guy who invented sport.

JOAN OF SHARK

The bravest shark who ever lived.

JOGGLING

Running and juggling at the same time.

JUPITERGH

One of the smelliest planets in the Solar System, this gas giant is composed entirely of burps. See also URANUS, ASSTRONOMERS and BERZERKCURY.

JUMPER SCAB

A blob of dried-up food on your favourite hoodie.

JU-SHIH TZU

A thin yet deadly dog trained in martial arts. See also NANJITSU.

RUMBLE IN THE KENNEL!!

PAWS OF FURY!!

HAAAAA!

Yaaaa!

HOUNDS HER ENEMIES!

SHE'LL KICK THE TZU OUT OF YOU!

Starring DOGGY CHAN!

HER BARK IS AS BAD AS HER BITE!

D

RATED D FOR DOGGY
CONTAINS BARKING, TAILS AND STICKCHASING
NOT SUITABLE FOR CATS!

K is for KARATE CHUCK, a spew so powerful it could chop a board in half. Takes years of training to master.

KANGAROOSTER

The rarely seen half kangaroo, half rooster. Can be identified by its call: 'Hopadoodledoo!'

KANGASPEW

To jump up and down until you vomit.

KARAOKEY DOKEY

The act of agreeing to something through song.

KEBABBLE

To talk with a mouthful of kebab.

KEBARBARA

The woman who invented kebabs.

KEYBORED

The feeling you get when you use a computer with really slow internet.

KICKELTY PICKLETY

A footy punt that goes in an unexpected direction.

KIDNAP TIME

The bit at the end of a hostage situation where everyone has a bit of shut-eye.

KIND-SIDED

That feeling when someone does something unexpectedly nice for you.

KISSEMBOWEL

To suck someone's guts out through the act of kissing. See also PSYCHOPASH.

KING PONG

A fart that smells exactly like a giant stressed-out gorilla.

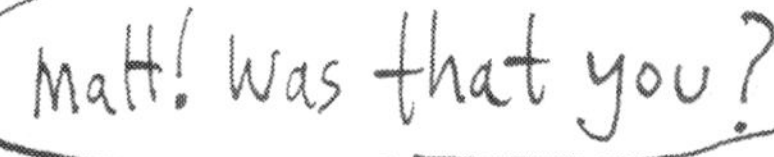

KISS AND SMELL

To kiss someone and accidentally fart at the same time.

KITTY LITTERATURE

Books cats like to read.

KLUTZ-BUSH, THE

The strange jerky dance performed by someone who is trying to hide the fact they just tripped over something. Sometimes performed at the same time as a MUMFUMBLE.

KNEEBRA

A bra for your knee.

KNEECAP

A hat you wear on your knee.

KNEEFLAP

When a scab on your knee hasn't quite come off yet and flaps about.

KIOSCARS, THE

An awards ceremony for people who run dodgy food kiosks. Awards are given for the worst customer service, the most expensive ice-cream and the most days gone by without changing the chip fat.

but, weirdly, that they were times less itchy than itching power. Eventually

KNEEPIT

The back part of your knee.

KNEWS, THE

A nightly TV information show about stuff you already knew.

KNIFE BEFORE XMAS, THE

A Christmas story your parents will refuse to tell you... See also XMAS WEE.

KNIGHTIE

Heavily armoured PJs worn in medieval times. They were extremely uncomfortable and the cause of many a bad knight's sleep.

KNIGHTRIDER

The world's first superhero.

KNITTER

Twitter for nans. Messages are knitted into a scarf and so can only be 140 characters long. See also NANNATECHNOLOGY.

KNOCK-NOT JOKES

Knock-knock jokes that don't make any sense whatsoever.

A koala

koalan

KNOCK-OUCH

When something hurts so much you can't think.

KRILLZONE

The trance-like state that whales go into before the feast. Can result in OVERKRILL.

KOALAN

The guy who invented koalas. See also RHINOCEROSS.

Don't go near Erica, she's in the KRILL ZONE today!

Grrrr!

KNOCK-NOT JOKES

KNOCK! KNOCK!
Who's there?
DR JONES.
Dr Jones who?
DR JONES, YOU HAVE CHRONIC DIARRHOEA AND WE HAVE TO CUT YOUR BUTT OFF.

KNOCK! KNOCK!
Who's there? Who's there? I said, who's there!? Oh, no one. They must've gone. That is so annoying.

KNOCK! KNOCK!
Who's there?
A DOOR.
A door who?
YES, I SAID A DOOR.
Yes, I heard you. Can I go now?
YES.
Thanks.

KNOCK! KNOCK!
Who's there?
KNOCKY.
Knocky who?
KNOCKY MCKNOCKY KNOCKER.
Go away.
OK.

KNOCK! KNOCK!
Who's there?
A GOLDFISH.
A goldfish who?
KNOCK! KNOCK!
Who's there?
A GOLDFISH.
A goldfish who?
KNOCK! KNOCK!
Who's there?
A GOLDFISH.
A goldfish who?
KNOCK! KNOCK!
Who's there?
A GOLDFISH

KNOCK! KNOCK!
Who's there
IVA
Iva who?
IVA SMITH, IS MALCOLM HOME?
There's no one here by that name.
OH, SORRY, I MUST HAVE THE WRONG HOUSE.
BYE.
BYE.

many things, including creams, most of them YELLUE in colour. She had to

L

L is for LUCKY CHUCKY, when you throw up into a wishing well.

LAFFTEAR

To laugh so much you cry. See also CRYDEA.

LAMBINATE

To squish something between two lambs.

LAMBOMETER

A device for detecting whether something is or isn't a lamb.

LAMBPOON

To mock a sheep.

LAMBTERN

A lamb that is so bright it illuminates everything around it.

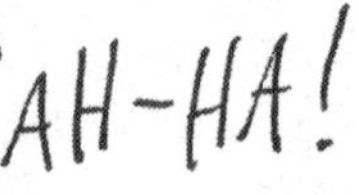

LAMINGTONNE

An ENBIGENATED lamington.

LASS SUE

The first person to tie a loop into a rope and swing it above their head.

LATRINO

Smaller than an atom and invisible to the human eye, the LATRINO is the tiniest particle the human nose can smell. Dads are particularly good at leaving LATRINO particles in the bathroom.

LAVENDUH

The stupidest flower.

LAWNATARIANISM

The movement against lawn mowing. Claiming that you are a LAWNATARIAN is an excellent way of avoiding chores – see our LIE-Q quiz.

LAXATIFF

To get into an argument with your bum.

LAZER BEANZ

A space-age food from the future that's great on toast.

LAZOO

To lasso something with lasers, a favourite party trick of FAILIENS.

LEG-OH!

The sound you make when you tread on a piece of Lego. See also ARCHIPELEGO.

LEODORANT

Underarm spray for lions.

LIAR ATTIRE

Any pair of pants that can easily be set on fire and worn while telling a fib.

Past Blast

THE LICE AGE

A period in history when everyone got head lice. To combat this it was agreed that everyone in the whole world should shave all of their hair off. Eventually the lice age passed and most people were able to begin growing their hair back, however a small number of people's hair follicles were so traumatised by the shaving that they refused to ever grow again. In fact if you look around now you can still see members of this hairless human species alive today, disguised in the forms of dads, uncles and grandads.

LICKR

An online photo gallery of tongues.

LICKTOES INTOLERANT

People who are allergic to licking toes. Tragically this is an affliction ruining the lives of more and more people every day.

LIDDITE

Someone who collects pen lids.

LIE-ON

Something or someone that looks like a lion but isn't.

LIE-Q

A test that measures how good you are at lying. FIBBACISTS score well.

What's your LIE-Q?

Answer these common questions with what you think is the best lie:

1. Why haven't you brushed your teeth?

A I am allergic to toothpaste.

B I did. But my gums, tongue and mouth are so dirty they make my teeth look gross again straightaway.

C I had my real teeth removed and then replaced with hologram ones that never need brushing, but thanks for asking.

2. Why didn't you do your homework?

A The dog ate my homework.

B The dog ate my homework and liked it so much she entered it into a reality TV cooking show for dogs called My Kennel Rules. She's famous now amongst dog gourmands.

C My homework ate the dog. I saw the whole thing. I'm too afraid to go near it. I don't wanna talk about it anymore. :(

3. Did you eat all the ice-cream?

A Yes, but ice-cream headaches can be fatal. So, actually, I saved the whole family. Let's go out for ice-cream to celebrate.

B Yes, but the doctor called and said that Dad has been diagnosed as lactose intolerant and I was trying to prevent him turning the house into a fart-filled NOSE-GO ZONE.

C YES! For I am none other than Softservia Neapolitana and I invented ice-cream, so I think I have a right to eat some once in a while.

4. Why haven't you loaded the dishwasher?

A I have, with air. Was there something else you wanted me to put in there?

B I forgot to do it because I have amnesia, Mum. Um... I mean... Who are you? Where am I? Why are all the dishes so dirty? Help me, I'm frightened.

C Because I wanted to talk to you first. I think we should move to a yearly washing-up roster. I have an opening in late November? How is that for you?

5. I thought I told you to mow the lawn?!

A Oh! I thought you said, 'Grow the lawn'. The English language is a funny thing.

B You only thought you did. What you actually told me to do was, 'Lie around all day and play video games'. So actually, I'm just doing what you told me to do.

C Excuse me, but I am a LAWNATARIAN and I believe mowing is cruel.

6. Did you make this mess?

A No, I did not. Nope, no way. Not at all. Never. In fact, I tidied up. Someone else made this mess, and when I find out who it was I'll give them a piece of my mind.

B Mess? Mess? This not a 'mess'. This is an art sculpture called <u>Everything from the Cupboards Moved onto the Floor</u>, Mixed Media, 2015.

C Yes, but it's a science experiment. They think I'm going to win a Nobel Prize and I think that you could be a little more supportive of my achievements.

Count up your scores to work out your LIE-Q.

Mostly As: You are a pretty terrible liar. You have a low LIE-Q. Don't become a car salesman, a professional poker player or a real estate agent.

Mostly Bs: You have an average Lie-Q. You can get out of most situations with liberal usage of untruths. But just a tip, next time you do a quiz, read the answers first and THEN answer the questions. That will significantly increase your LIE-Q.

Mostly Cs: You have a high LIE-Q. You should probably think about becoming a FIBBACIST.

Mostly Ds: You've completely lied about your answers . . . congratulations! You rival GOLIARTH in your fibbing skills.

They thought it worked. But, on the day of her **90**th birthday she accidentally counted the

LIGHTHOWS?

The questions people always ask about lighthouses, like: How do they get beds up those stairs? Do you ever get dizzy? How do they change the bulbs? Do you ever make enormous shadow puppets? Is all the furniture round? Is it, like, the coolest place to live ever?

Dare me to DROP PLOP?

LIMPLE

A zit you squeeze and hardly any gunk comes out.

LOLLIPLOP

Poo on a stick.

L.O.L.O

Laugh Out Loud Outside.

LOOGIES, THE

An award given to the celebrity with the nicest toilet.

I'll NEVER surrender!

LOO LURKER

A turd that refuses to be flushed.

LOOPEE

When you need to wee so badly you go completely crazy. This can occur in a HOLDON during a long car trip.

LUCK OF THE DRAWERS

The special power given to you by your lucky underpants.

Cate Blanchett's oscar underpants.

Amelia Earhart's flying bloomers.

Neil Armstrong's moon landing undies

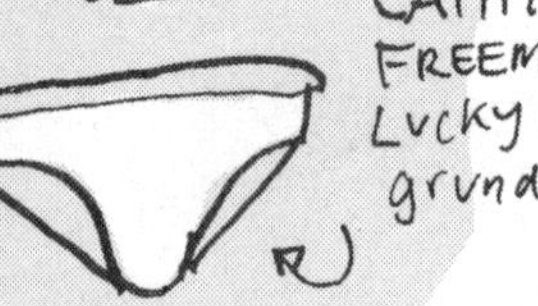

CATHY FREEMAN'S Lucky grundies.

Sir Edmund Hillary's Everest jocks.

Barack Obama's election-night pair.

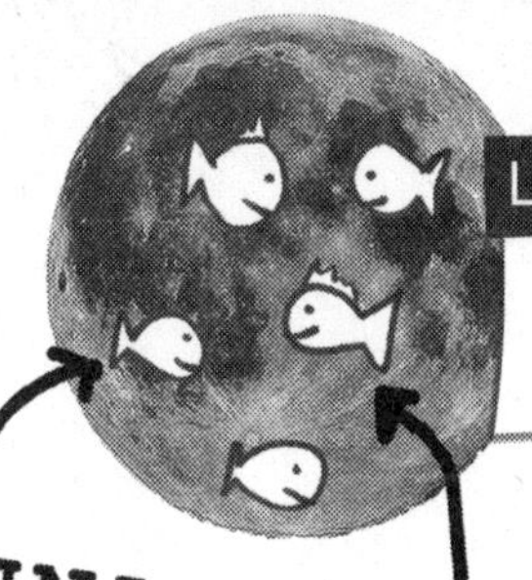

LUNA TUNA

A species of fish found only in the moon's Sea of Tranquility.

LUNCH TIM

The guy who invented lunch. Before him, people were starving until dinner. Good old Lunch Tim.

Heston Bloominhell*!
SIGNATURE DISHES....
*WORST CHEF EVER

THE LYCHEESE!
cheddar
Lychee

RICE
DUST SUSHI
seaweed
DUST

WEEDS SALAD
WEEDS
SALAD BOWL

LYCHEESE

The worst dessert ever. A combination of lychee, ice-cream and cheddar cheese, invented by the famous chef Heston Bloominhell, a molecular grosstronomer.

M

M is for MONKEY WRETCH, when you vomit up banana, or when you vomit on a monkey.

MACAROOMI

A cubbyhouse made out of pasta.

MADVERTISEMENT

An ad on TV that is on so much you literally go crazy.

maggots queuing

can't wait

INSIDE!

THE OLDEST CHEESE SANDWICH IN HISTORY!

Bryan Ritchie, magnit collector

MAGOTTEN

Something that's been left so long it's now wriggling with maggots.

MAGNIT

A piece of gunk that sticks to your hair.

MANIQUINTET

A group of (five) singing shop mannequins. See also QUINCETET.

MANIYACK

Someone who's talking crazy.

MARCO POOLOO

A game you play in the pool where everyone is blindfolded, the person who is 'it' does a SWIMMING POO, and everyone else has to swim around trying to avoid touching it. Disgusting, but fun.

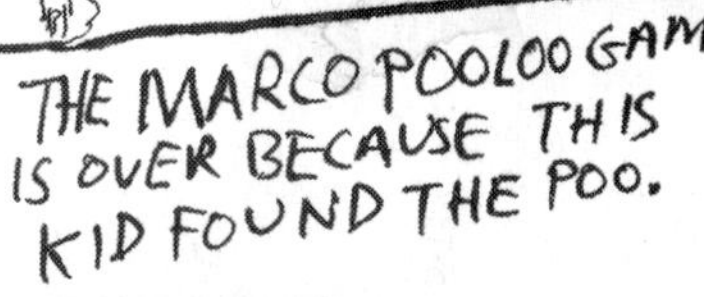

MASSACARA

When make-up goes horribly wrong.

MARATHONG

A famous Australian event where you run 42.195 km on a hot beach in bare feet to get to your thongs.

MARSHSMELLOWS

Marshmallows that come in horrible flavours and smell gross. Do not toast them on the campfire.

MATHEMATIC-TACS

Working out a maths problem by eating lollies.

MARTIAL SMARTS

A brain-training technique that teaches you that it's much easier to chop a bit of wood in half with a saw than with your head. See also THONG-DO.

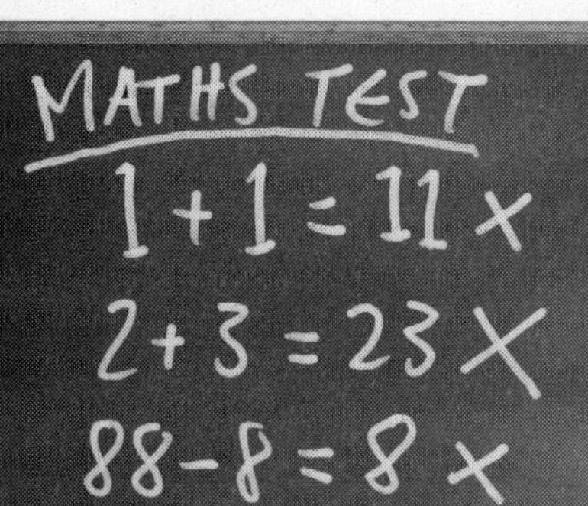

MATHSTAKE

To calculate something incorrectly.

MEATEORITE

A piece of meat that has been chewed up and spat out.

MEALS ON SEALS

A food-delivery service run by seals for people who live on boats. While they mean well, the seals can be a bit over-enthusiastic, kissing hello as they deliver the food and causing people to occasionally exclaim 'MY LIPS ARE SEALED'!

MEGABITE

To take a bigger bite of something than you should.

MEHLON

A melon that's, like, 'meh'.

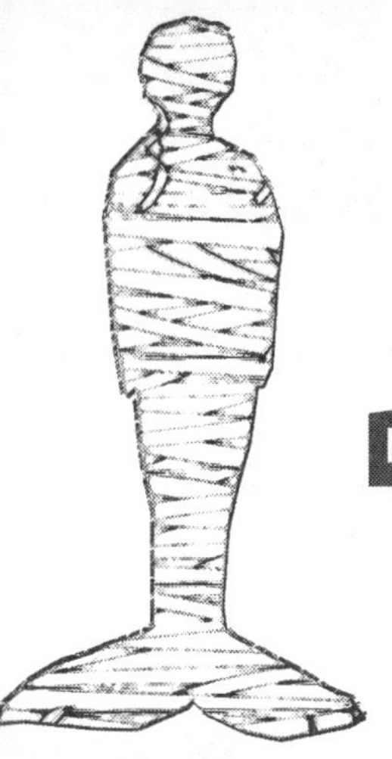

MERMUMMIE

A mummified mermaid.

Past Blast

MESSOPOTAMIA

One of the earliest civilisations in history, the MESSOPOTAMIAN Empire was also one of the most untidy. The MESSOPOTAMIAN civilisation began around 3200 BCE (Before Cleaning Existed) and it was a complete shambles: people were always tripping over stone tablets that had been left lying around, and dropping their clay pots. This is why all that archaeologists find now are bits of broken crockery. Perhaps the worst part of MESSOPOTAMIA was that no one ever washed up. It got so bad that a Messopotamian person invented writing just so they could leave a note in the kitchen that said: 'There is no dishwashing fairy. Please do your own washing up.' Unfortunately no one had learned to read yet so the note was ineffective.

*MESSOPOTAMIAN for really, really untidy.

THE MEWS...

MEWS, THE

The news presented by cats, for cats, about cats.

MIAOWCH!

What a cat says when it stubs its paw.

MINIPHONE

A tiny megaphone that ants use to direct movies.

MISSLETOE

When a toe is used as a missile. See also TOENAIL GUN.

Past Blast

MIDDLING AGES, THE

This was the most sensible and average period in history. Things that happened were the Grey Death, the Pretty Big Fire of London, the Rule of Alfred the All Right, the invention of egg sandwiches, the 100 Minutes War, and the discovery of toothpaste.

or an ICE-DREAM CONE with different flavours, all of which are your favourite,

Other TV shows you may have missed:

A Currant Affair: A hard-hitting investigative journalism show about issues concerning dried fruit. Great date-night viewing.

Border Pootrol: A fly-on-the-wall series following the ins and outs of an airport toilet. Actually, mostly the outs.

The Blockage: Watch celebrities plunge the toilets of everyday people.

Master Cliff: A cooking show set halfway up the world's steepest mountain.

Doctor Poo: The good Doctor travels through time and space to solve mysteries, look dapper and flush away evil in his Portaloo Turdis.

Giggle and Toot: A 10-hour montage of videos of people laughing at their own farts.

Bananas without Pyjamas: No one knows what this show was about because it was banned before it ever went to air.

MOLLARS

Money left in exchange for teeth.

MONOLOOGING

Talking to yourself on the toilet.

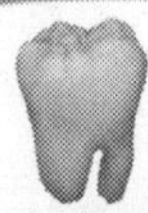

MOOGLE

What cows use to search the internet.

MOON RIVER

A song about a man who shows his bum to a river. Made famous by singer Frank Sinasstra.

a long-lost relative and when you get inside you find out it's **100**% pure gold and you are

MOOSICAL

A stage show starring singing and dancing cows. Not as entertaining as they sound, moosicals are mainly about things that cows love. Some titles include Milk! Grass! and Chewing!

MOTHERBORED

The glazed-over look on a mum's face when you talk about your favourite computer game.

MOUTH FART

A burp so smelly it may as well be a fart. For other kinds of burps see page 22.

MUMFUMBLE

When your mum drops something.

MUDFRIGHT

The shock of discovering that tne sticky brown stuff on your shoe is not mud. See also VEGEMIGHT?

MUSICK

A feeling that can come over you when you hear music you don't like.

MY LIPS ARE SEALED

When you have kissed a seal and your breath smells of fish. See also MEALS ON SEALS.

MYSTERWEE

When you don't know if you need to wee or not.

MYSTHAIRY

When something is strangely hairy, like a fly, a cat's tongue or your dad's back.

N

N is for NOSE BERRIES, the bits of spew that get caught in your nose.

NACHOLEPSY

To fall asleep face-down in your nachos. This can happen shortly after falling into a VORTEX-MEX.

NAIL JAM

The black stuff that mysteriously appears under your fingernails. Even though it may seem a similar consistency to other condiments, it is not a good idea to eat it.

NAMESAMER

A person with the same name as you. First NAMESAMERs are pretty common. First and last NAMESAMERs are rare but not unheard of. If you ever meet a first, last and middle NAMESAMER the universe will collapse and then explode. Probably.

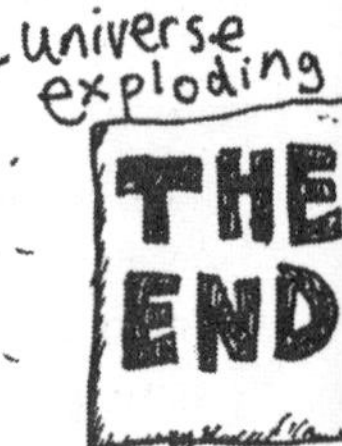

HOME OFFICE STUFF

er ma'am, are you going to buy that?

KIEA

HA!

SMASH!

$LOTS

NANJITSU

The ancient and secret art of nanna martial arts, including the technique of THONG-DO.

NANNA JAM

To be blocked in by nannas – this can happen at buffet tables and any place where there is free tea and coffee.

NANNATECHNOLOGY

Technology made by nans for nans. See also KNITTER and INSTAGRAN.

NANURP

A nanna burp. There are a whole family of burps:
a murp (mum burp),
a durp (dad burp),
a step-durp (step-dad burp), and a dogurp (a dog burp).

NANSTACHE

The totally excellent hair that grows on your nanna's top lip.

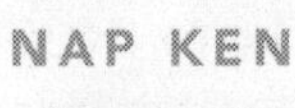

NAP KEN

The guy who invented wiping your face with a piece of paper after dinner. He was dating KEBARBARA at the time.

NARCISSCYST

Someone who thinks their pimples are better than everybody else's.

NAYBOURS

A long-running TV soap based on a bunch of horses that live next door to each other. Hardly any horses watch it anymore but it's still popular in England.

NICE LEA

The world's most generous person. If you ever need anything at all, you only need to ask NICE LEA.

NIGHTINGFAIL

A song bird with a terrible singing voice.

NO-IT-ALL

A person who says 'no' to everything, even to things that are absolutely UN-NO-ABLE.

NERVOUS BREAKDANCE

To go crazy on a dance floor.

NOSE-GO ZONE

A place too smelly to visit, like a rubbish tip, sewage works or the toilet after your mum/dad/brother/sister/ dog/next-door neighbour/horse/ football team/whole population of New Zealand has used it. The cleaning of a NOSE-GO ZONE is worth at least fifty YUCK BUCKS, and even more if it is the day after curry night.

NOSE GRASS

Hair that grows out of an old person's nose. Why this happens is a MYSTHAIRY. NOSE GRASS is closely related to TOESTACHES and HAIRY-FLOSS.

NOSTRILDAMAS

A nose that can predict the future.

NPS

Nan-positioning system. Used to find lost nannas in supermarkets.

NUDELING

To wander around the house naked. Dads can often be seen NUDELING on their way to and from the shower. Babies and younger brothers and sisters can often be seen NUDELING in the backyard under the sprinkler.

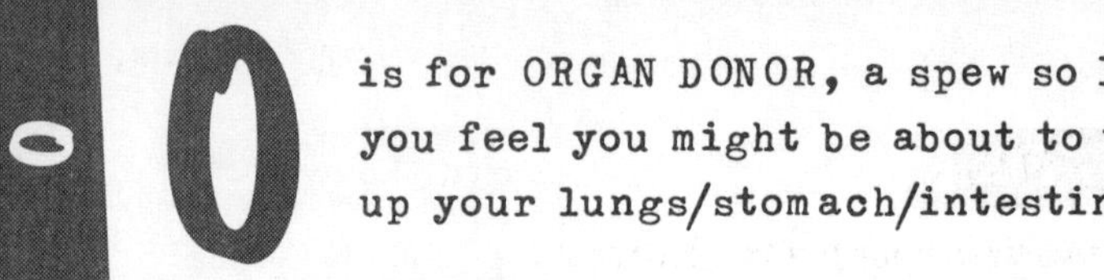

O is for ORGAN DONOR, a spew so large you feel you might be about to throw up your lungs/stomach/intestines.

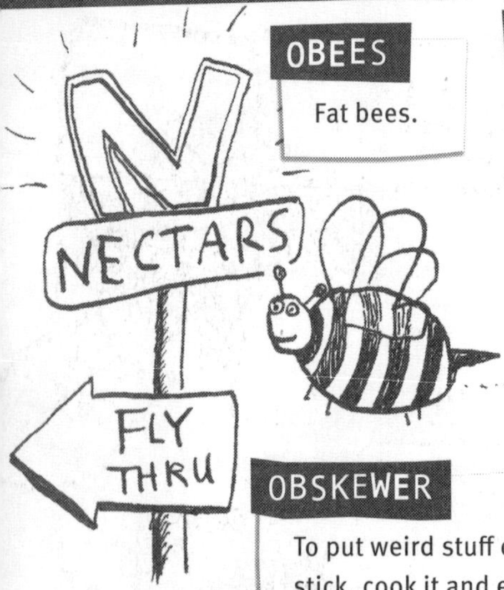

OBEES

Fat bees.

OBJETS DE FART

Beautiful vintage farts used to decorate the home.

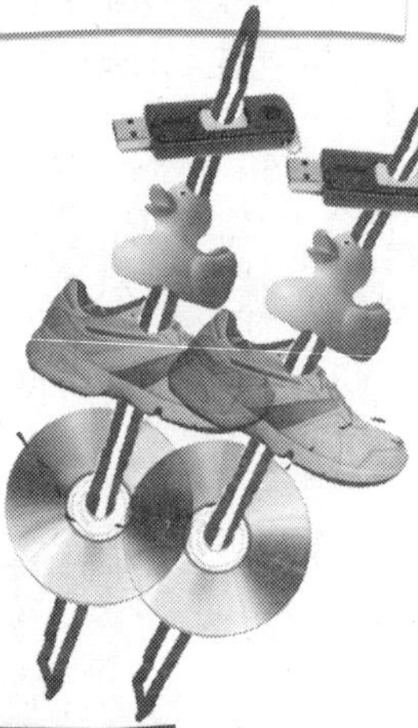

NECTARS

FLY THRU

OBSKEWER

To put weird stuff on a stick, cook it and eat it.

OCTAGONE

Any eight-sided shape that isn't there.

OCTOPUS, THE

A legendary eight-headed pimple. The person who had it was a complete NARCISSCYST.

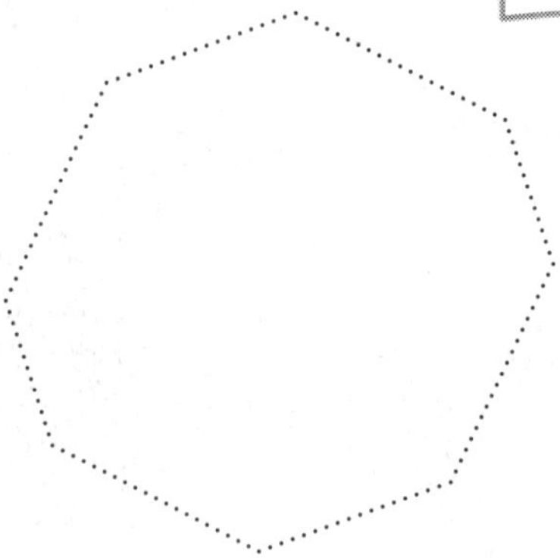

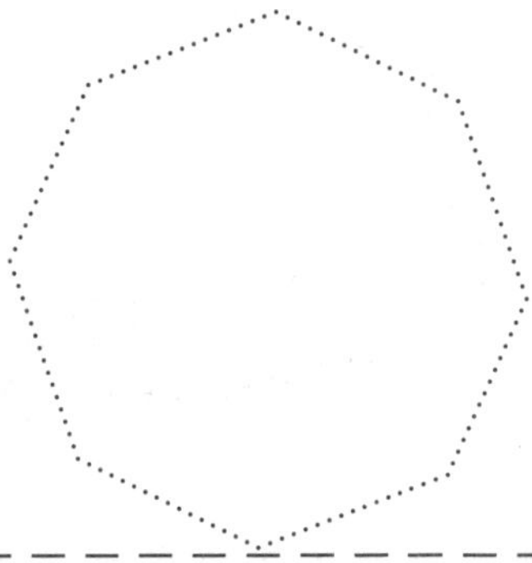

order **106** pizzas to be delivered (none of which have been FRUINed)

ODOURANT

The short-lived opposite to deodorant. A popular brand in Australia is Stynx.

OFFALL

To trip over someone's guts.

OFFENDEAD

To be so offended by something you actually die. May occur whilst reading ICKYPEDIA.

OFFISHAL

A really important fish.

OFFLOOKER

Someone who wasn't watching.

OFFOMATOPOEIA

Words that are spelt nothing like they sound, like receipt, handkerchief and wrinkle. See also INGLISH.

OLIVESPOIL

When you get a delicious pizza and discover someone has put olives on it! A savoury version of FRUIN.

ON THE TIP OF MY BUM

When you are trying to fart but can't.

OOPSY DAISY

History's little-known most clumsy person. It was rumoured she was so clumsy she could drop something that was already on the ground.

OPENISH

When a shop is supposed to be open but actually isn't. You can tell a shop is openish when a sign is stuck to the door that says, 'Back in 10 mins'.

ORANGUTANGLE

A confusing mess of apes.

ORIGAMI HARMI

To you give yourself a paper cut trying to make one of those Japanese cranes.

ORIGIN AL

The first ever human being; it is not clear whether Origin Al was a male or a female, as it could have been short for Alice, Alison, Aloysius, Ang, Ahmed, Albie, Alan or Albert.

ORIFACES

The collective word for the holes in your head.

OVERDOZE

To sleep for too long.

OVERKRILL

The feeling a whale gets when it's eaten too much. Can happen on WHALENTINES DAY.

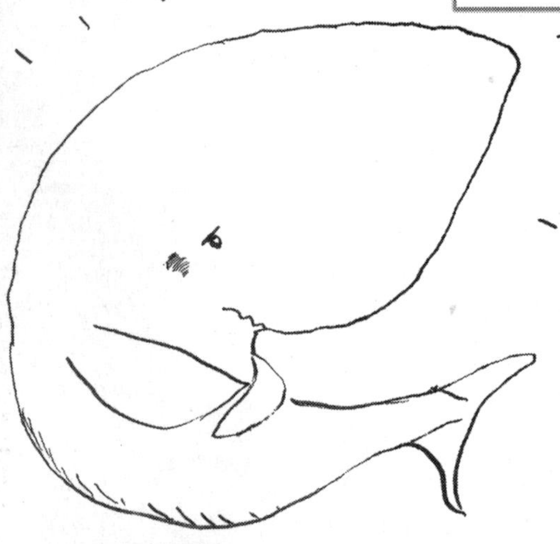

OZONESLAYER

The worst fart you could ever do. A fart so powerful it's off the DECISMELL scale.

Feel better? Fact: This is not the first ever counting book. **111** years ago a person with

P

P is for PUKULELE, a small instrument that makes you throw up when you hear it played.

PANDAMONIUM

When pandas freak out.

PARENTHETICAL QUESTION

Questions your parents ask that are impossible to answer, like 'How many times do I have to tell you?' and 'If all your friends jumped off a cliff would you do it too?'

PASTWORD

A password you have forgotten.

PEE-MAIL

To write a message to someone in the snow.

P.E. TEACHER

A Probably Evil Teacher. P.E. TEACHERs often win lots of awards at the TEACH-ARGGGHS!

PHEWTURE

The moment in time when life starts looking up. Generally around 3pm on a Friday.

PICKTURE

A photograph of someone digging for snot balls in their schnozz.

PIRAHNANANA

A banana that eats you.

Attack of the ...

...PIRAHNANANA!

RAAAAH!!

POLAR BARE

A nude polar bear.

CENSORED!

books, a whole set of them. Originally there were **113** books, and each of them

POLLYGONE

A four-sided object you put dead birds in.

POOETRY

Really bad poems.

POOOOL

A swimming pool completely full of poo. Can occur when so many SWIMMING POOs are done that the game of MARCO POOLOO is impossible.

POOPULAR

Popular pooing places, like the dunny (if you are Australian), in nappies (if you are a baby), and on people's heads (if you are a bird or a helicopter pilot). See also DROP PLOP.

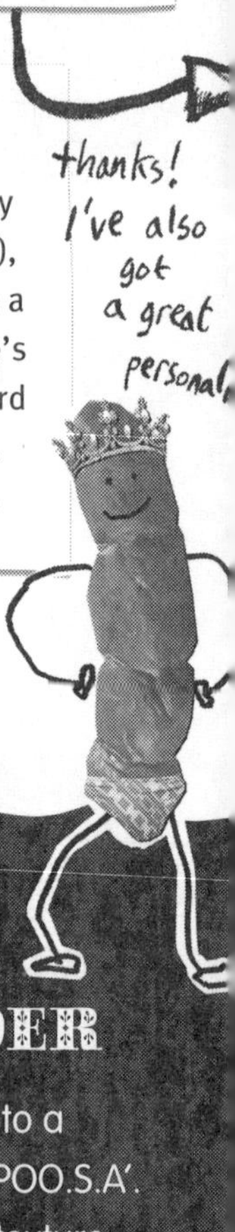

POOTIFUL

A beautiful poo. See also SPEWTIFUL.

POOTY IS IN THE EYE OF THE BEHOLDER

Until very recently, people entered their business into a controversial beauty pageant called 'Miss and Mr POO.S.A'. Poos were judged on three categories: stinkiness, texture and swimsuit. The competition was eventually shut down by protestors who believed that what a poo looks like on the outside isn't important. It's what's inside the poo that counts!

POOETRY

E. MOTIONAL

had exactly **115** sentences, and each of these sentences

FEELINGS

By E. Motional

Feelings.
I have lots of feelings.
These feelings that I'm feeling
make me feel feelings.
And that makes me feel feelings.
The End

had exactly **116** words and each of these words

ALPHABETTI SPAGHETTI POEM

by E. Motional

I asked the alphabetti spaghetti:
What should I do with my life?

It said:
aesgif fowoh oihg coihc iugh
cnbio niopmc hciyq jc.

Thanks a lot, alphabetti spaghetti.

BOXED IN

by E. Motional

Darkness. Blackness.
Mine eyes cannot see!
Scared. Trapped. No escape.
Cold. Damp.
Frozen peas?
Help, I'm in a freezer.

LIFE

By E. Motional

Life is sometimes good.
Life is sometimes bad.
#problems

FLOWERS

by E. Motional

Roses are red, violets are blue.
But are they edible?
Argh! Ergh! Phtewey! Ack!
No, they aren't.

no words with that many letters, or even letters. That's just too many letters for a word. So, it was clea

THE MICROWAVE OF LOVE
by E. Motional

Round and around and around and around,
Round and around and around and around,
Round and around and around and around,
Round and around and around and around,
Round and around and around and around,
Round and around and around and around,

Round and around and around and around,
Round and around and around and around,
Round and around and around and around,
PING!
I'm done.

ODE TO THE MOON
by E. Motional

Oh moon! Oh moon!
Oh moony moon!
Something something something June.
Poems are hard.
I'm hungry.
Bye.

INSOMNIA

by E. Motional

Why can't I sleep?
Why can't I sleep?
Why can't I sleep?
Why can't I sleep?
Oh, it's 1pm.

and started inventing new words, some of which were **120** letters long and took

WHAT MY HEART IS LIKE

by E. Motional

My heart is clogged,
Like a toilet that won't flush.
Call the plumber, please.
The plumber of feelings.

My heart is bare,
Like a streaker at the football.
Put on pants.
The pants of love.

My heart is frozen,
Like the polar ice cap.
Melt it like global warming.
The global warming of your beauty.

My heart is wounded,
Like King Harold's eye in 1066.
Only the arrow is your harsh words
  and the eye is my emotions.

just over **121** minutes to say out loud. Imagine inventing new words and

numbers – people would think you were **122** % insane to do that. They would also think

POOT-POOT GOLF

Like putt-putt golf but, instead of using putters, the ball is moved by farting at it.

POOTRAITE

To make a portrait of someone out of poo.

POPPING ON

To fart in reverse. When your bum sucks air in.

POSTWICH

To send a sandwich in the mail.

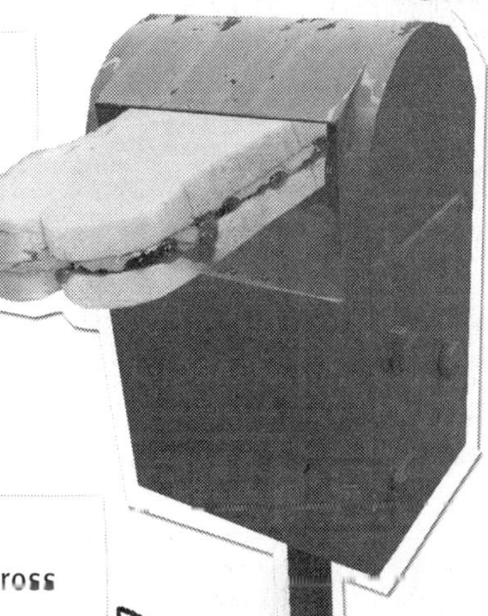

PRUB

To burp backwards. See also POPPING ON.

PSYCHOPASH

When your parents make out! #gross

PURRFUME

Deodorant for cats. It smells slightly of wee. See also LEODORANT.

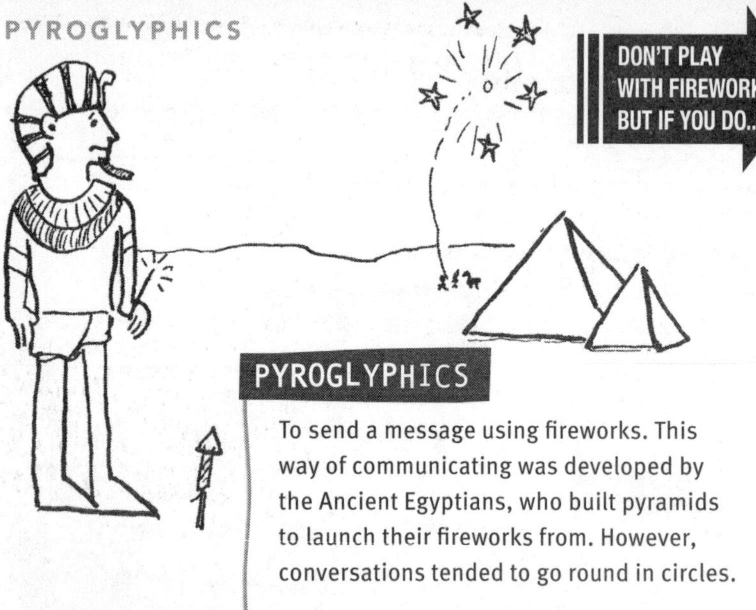

DON'T PLAY WITH FIREWORKS. BUT IF YOU DO...

PYROGLYPHICS

To send a message using fireworks. This way of communicating was developed by the Ancient Egyptians, who built pyramids to launch their fireworks from. However, conversations tended to go round in circles.

Here is a translated PYROGLYPHIC communication between two Ancient Egyptians, Ramses and his next-door neighbour Danielle.

Ramses: Stop making loud explody sounds!
Danielle: You stop making loud explody sounds.
Ramses: No, you stop.
Danielle: No, you stop.
Ramses: I will if you will.
Danielle: OK . . . there, see I stopped.
Ramses: No you didn't!
Danielle: You didn't either!
Ramses: On the count of 3 let's stop, all right?
Danielle: OK. Ready? 1, 2, 3 . . .
Ramses: See, I stopped properly this time.
Danielle: NO YOU DID NOT.
Ramses: WELL YOU DIDN'T EITHER.
Danielle: This time I will.
Ramses: Promise?
Danielle: Yes. Ready . . .

These conversations were known to last for days on end.

The Counting Book™ contains perfectly normal numbers like **125** (which can be written as one hundred and twenty-five) or

the number **126** (which can be written as one hundred and twenty-six) or

ORANGUTANGLE QUADWRANGLE

QUADWRANGLE

To arrange things into groups of four.

4 DUCKS!

IMQO!

QUAGMYER

To get really lost in a department store.

QUAKEL

A duck's laugh.

QUANTUMMM?

What scientists say when they can't think of an answer. See also ENCYCLOPEDIUMMM?

QUANTUMMY PHYSICS

The study of how people always have room for dessert.

there are too many ducks on this page!

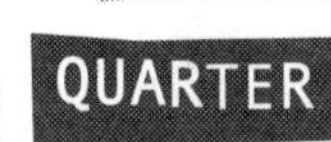

QUARK

What a posh duck says.

QUARTER SLAUGHTER

A dramatic change in the footy score between quarters. Can be the result of too many KICKLETY PICKLETYs.

QUEEN OF FARTS

A controversial poem about a queen popping one off in the throne room.

one hundred and twenty-eight because **128** is written like that already). It can also be helpful in solving

QUEENY WEENY

A small monarch.

QUESTSHUN

A question asked but ignored.

QUEUE TURN

When you see a long queue and decide not to join it. Can sometimes happen when you see a really long BBQUEUE.

QUEUEBEC

A really small city in Canada you have to queue up for ages to get in to.

QUICHE LORRAINE

The woman who invented the idea that you can have eggs for dinner.

QUICK

What ducks say in New Zealand.

QUICKSTAND

When the kickstand on your bike keeps sinking into the mud.

QUICKPICNIC

Swiftly removing a booger from your nose and eating it. Doing this can prevent someone snapping a PICKTURE.

QUINCETET

Five musicians playing chamber music with fruit.

QUIZ FIZZ

The feeling in the stomach you get when your teacher announces a surprise test. This sickly feeling is often the cause of MATHSTAKES.

QUIRKY JERKY

Strange bits of dried meat.

QUIZARD

Someone who's really good at quizzes.

QUOCK

A duck swear word. See also QOL.

QWAZY

What you would have to be to read this far into this book! You're our new bestie.

QWHALE

An enormous bird.

R is for RAINBLOW CHUNKS, colourful vomit.

R.I.PEE

An engraving reserved for the gravestones of those who've died from doing dangerous wee-related things.

R.I.Pee.
Here lies BILL BUSTING
He held on as long as he could.

RABBYTE

A rabbi with extra-good computer smarts.

RABIECHINO

To spew babychino out of your mouth so it looks like you've got rabies.

RACQUIET

A very quiet tennis racquet developed for the sport 'Sleep Tennis', an incredibly boring game designed to send the viewing public, umpires, players and commentators to sleep. See also SCOREBORED.

RADISH

Something that is sort of, but not quite, rad.

RALPHABET

A collection of all the different ways of spewing in alphabetical order. See the start of every letter in ICKYPEDIA.

RAPPING PAPER

Stuff hip-hop MCs use to put their birthday pressies in, yo.

RATTLECAKE

A birthday cake with a snakey centre.

RAZZAMA-TASSIE

Something fancy that comes from Tasmania.

REARING AID

Something you sit on to muffle the sound of your farts.

The latest in rearing aid technology can be seen here

REBURPERATE

A burp so loud it makes all the objects and people around it vibrate.

RECESSPIT

The part at the bottom of your school bag that's full of mouldy, uneaten snacks. Look here to find key ingredients for a BRAT-WORST Bag Snag.

Elspeth MacFluff's
NEW!
FART MUFFLE® TECHNOLOGY
REARING AIDS!
Reduces Fart Noise by 80%!
one size fits all Bums!
CALL 1800-SBD TODAY!
I was always worried about the volume of my bottom burps. But now I have a Rearing Aid I don't have to care!

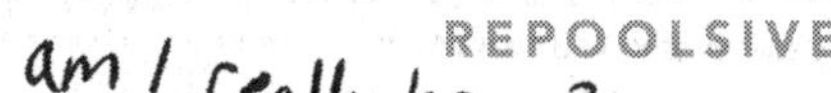

RENÉ DESFARTES

A French SMELLOSOPHER.

'I stink, therefore I am'

Whilst pondering the problem of whether or not he existed, RENÉ DESFARTES crunked one off. He suddenly realised that if he was able to make a room smell that bad then he must, in fact, exist. This phrase 'I stink, therefore I am' is now known by SMELLOSOPHERS as 'Cognito Ergo Bum'. See also REVOLTAIRE.

REHASH BROWNS

To reuse an uneaten hash brown for some other purpose, like a doorstop, mouse pad or eraser.

REPOOLSIVE

A swimming pool that has gone green over winter. A pool can also easily become REPOOLSIVE if it is not cleaned properly after a game of MARCO POOLOO. See also POOOOL.

REPULSIEVE

A device for straining the chunks out of vomit.

REVOLTAIRE

A 17th-Century French SMELLOSOPHER famous for his edict: 'I may not like the smell of your farts but I will defend to the death your right to do them.'

RHINOCEROSS

The guy who invented rhinoceroses.

RINGTERRUPTION

When someone's phone goes off at a really bad time, like during a play, in the movies or at a funeral.

RIOT SQUID

An octopus used to break up a protest.

RISSOTOES

The fluff that accumulates between your toes. See also NAIL JAM.

ROBUTT

A mechanical butt for people who have had their real ones amputated. The more expensive models come with built-in REARING AIDS.

Past Blast

ROMAN UMMMPIRE, THE

When the Romans first discovered that their superior military knowledge and naval prowess allowed them to take over the world, they couldn't decide if they wanted to or not. This period of history was called the ROMAN UMMMPIRE. For further reading see the book *Err, Claudius?*

ROTTON BUDS

Used cotton buds covered in EAR SPEW.

RUBBISHAREA

A large island in the middle of the Pacific that's made out of the all the garbage that has washed into the sea.

A postcard from RubbishArea!

RONDONKULOUS, RIDICOOLOSS, RE-DIC-LEE-US

Ridiculous spellings of 'ridiculous'. See also INGLISH.

who lived at number 138 Scabby Road, which is

Like when you peel off a scab
The potent mix of old banana skins, unwashed socks, stale farts and dirty crockery has caused a chemical reaction and has burst into flames!
"I can't see! my eyes! my eyes!"
Like just after a brutal medieval battle
It is impossible to clean your room... Therefore...
COOL!
DON'T CLEAN YOUR ROOM!
Put out the fire
NO
Ask the government to clean it up
Call a demolition company. Can they blast their way in with dynamite?
YES
NO!
Build a pillow fort in the loungeroom and sleep there.
YES
The wall?
CLEAN YOUR ROOM!
Can you get in through the window?
NO!
Unicorn
Rainbow

S is for SPEWPOCOLYPSE, when there is so much vomit it feels like the world is ending.

SALAMEH

A salami that's, like, meh. See also MEHLON.

SARCOUGHYGAS

When someone farts in a sealed room.

SAUSAGE DRIZZLE

A BBQ that gets rained out.

SAYONNAISE

The white stuff that develops in the corner of people's mouths when they talk too much. See also CHATTER SPLATTER.

SCABULOUS

An awesome scab.

to number 140 Scabby Road and diagonally

SCAREWEE

When you get so frightened a little bit of wee comes out.

SCLOOP

To scoop up gloop.

SCOREBORED

That feeling you get when someone is talking about a sport you're not interested in. Can happen when people tell you about their new RAQUIET.

SEAGULLIBLE

A seagull who'll eat anything, believing it's a chip.

SELFIE-INFLICTED INJURY

To hurt oneself while taking a selfie.

SHARKITECT

Someone who designs houses for sharks.

SHIP FOR BRAINS

Someone who is obsessed with boats.

SHOP TILL YOU POP

To get so bored while shopping that you literally explode.

to number **142** Scabby Road (which is our house, feel free to come visit).

SHUFFLE POP

To sneak away from a stinky fart.

SIBLING QUIBBLING

When you fight with your brothers and sisters.

SLIPUP

When you accidentally hiccup.

SLURPRISE

An unexpected lump you suck up through a straw. See also ICEBURGER.

Anyway, they told us that the man who lives at number **143**, who looks like

Small

Smedium

medium

mediumer

mediumerest

SMEDIUM

Not small, but not medium either.

other sizes: A handy guide!

Regular
Tiny
Teeny-tiny
Smallerer
Blobby
Teensy
Teensy-tiny
Not even there

SMELFIE

To take a photo of your toilet. The LOOGIES are judged via celebs submitting SMELFIES.

SMELL CHECK

To sniff an item of clothing before wearing it.

The world's dirtiest DAD SAGS: Do not SMELL CHECK!!!

SMELLOSOPHER

Someone who thinks too much about farts. See RENÉ DESFARTES and REVOLTAIRE.

SMELLUCINATE

To smell something that isn't really there.

SMORGASBORED

A lot of really boring food.

SNACKTASTROPHY

When someone else eats a snack you've been saving.

SNAP CHAT

What crocodiles use to text.

SNEEZE BOW

The beautiful rainbow effect caused by sneezing on a computer screen.

SNOT NESS MONSTER

Hideous sticky creatures that live under chairs and tables and feed off the boogers people wipe there.

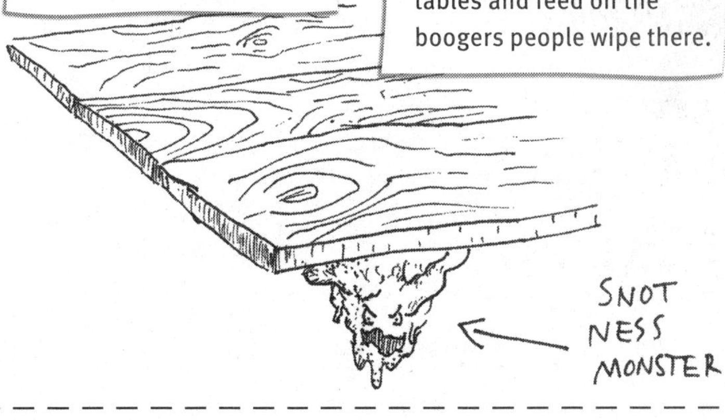

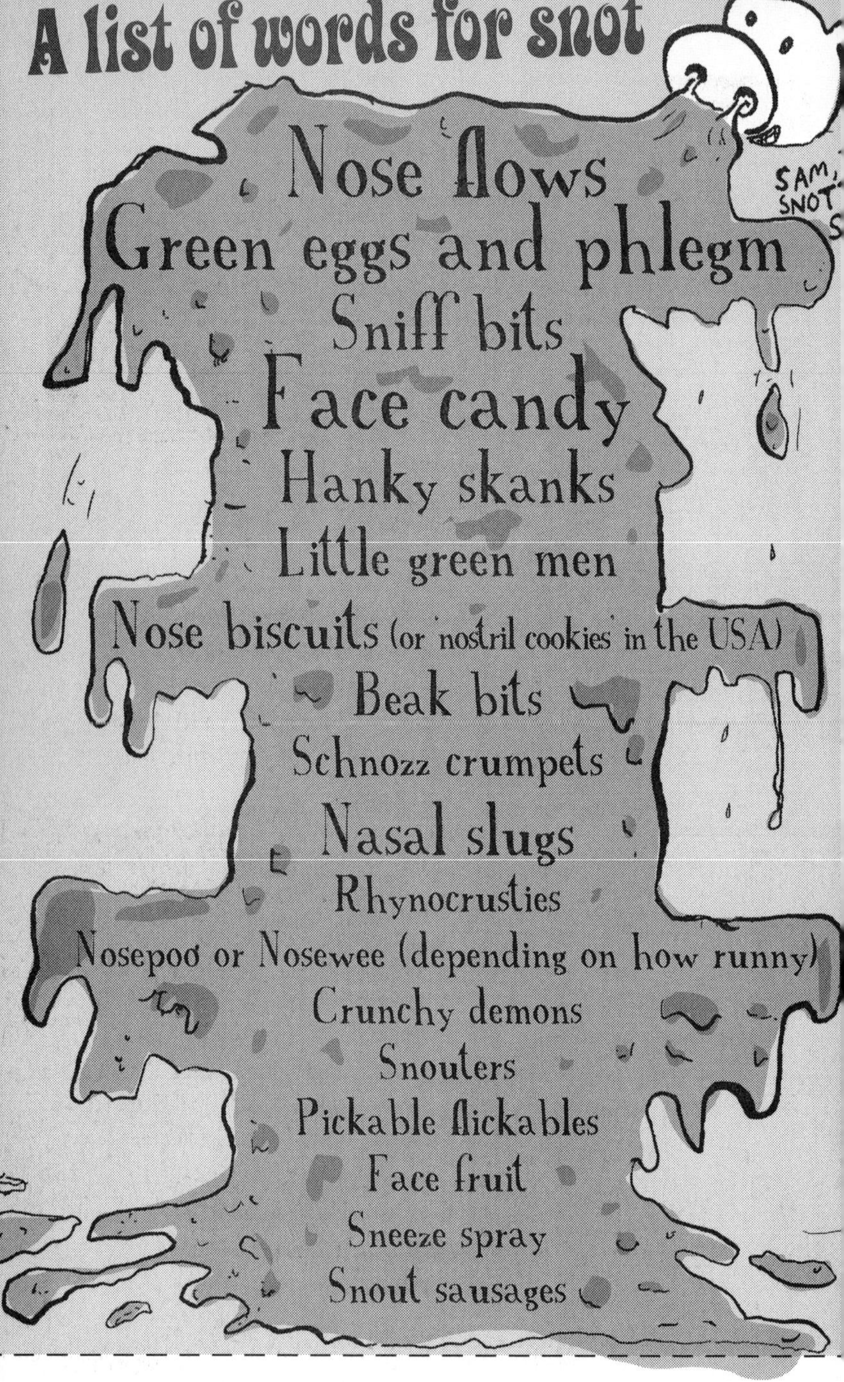
A list of words for snot
SAM,
SNOT
Nose flows
Green eggs and phlegm
Sniff bits
Face candy
Hanky skanks
Little green men
Nose biscuits (or 'nostril cookies' in the USA)
Beak bits
Schnozz crumpets
Nasal slugs
Rhynocrusties
Nosepoo or Nosewee (depending on how runny)
Crunchy demons
Snouters
Pickable flickables
Face fruit
Sneeze spray
Snout sausages

SNOTBOX

A box in which to keep all your favourite boogers. Snotboxes are used to stop people wiping their boogers under the school chair or blowing them into a hanky.

SOCIAL BURPER

Someone who isn't afraid to burp in public.

SONIC EWETH

A famous sheep band from the 90s.

SOUPERSTITION

To have a feeling you're not going to like what's in the soup you've been given.

SPACEPOOT

To let rip in a space suit.

Matt did you eat the whole cake?

No!... and by 'no!' I mean YES!

In fact I don't feel great...

Wait! I'll get you....

...a bag

BLEURGH!

Whoops #soz

I do feel better though!

oh oh!

HUEY!

BARF!

RALPH!

SPEW OFF!

OH DEAR......

SPEW-OFF

Like a dance-off but with spew.

SPEWTIFUL

A beautiful spew.

SPIHIDER

A spider that is really good at hiding.

SPILLCHILL

When you spill something cold on your pants.

So the question that was asked **148** times was, 'Who did?'

SPIT BITS

The flecks of spit that fly out of super-excited or super-angry people. See also CHATTER SPLATTER.

SPONTANEOUS COMBUMTION

In the unlikely event that a person never ever farts, the massive build-up of a lifetime of gas can cause a highly dangerous SPONTANEOUS COMBUMTION to occur. The explosion is so severe that the bum is blown clean off the body with potentially fatal consequences. This is an occupational hazard for librarians, lift operators, astronauts and any occupation where farting is discouraged. See also SPACEPOOT.

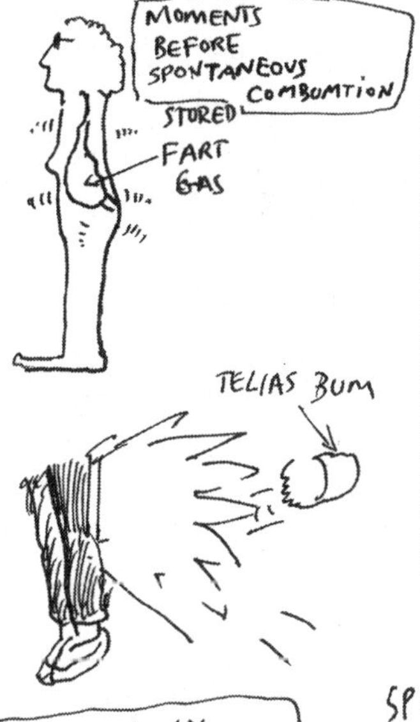

UNTIL FINALLY.....
SPONTANEOUS CONBUMTION!
KERBLAM!
TELIA'S BUM
AHHH!
GAAAS!
BOOOM!
PAAAARP!
AAAH!
ICKY PEDIA
YEARS OF GAS

And he replied **149** times that he didn't know, but to produce a stink so foul it

SQWERTY KEYBOARD

Part keyboard, part waterpistol. See also INVENTSHUNS.

SULTANA CLAUS

A mythical man who travels around the world FRUINing cakes by putting fruit in them. See also FRUIN.

SUPER BLOOPER

When you really mess something up.

SWEATEA

A delicious hot drink made from throwing all your sports clothes, including sneakers, into a saucepan and boiling them for an hour. Best enjoyed alongside a piping hot BRAT-WORST.

SWIMMING POO

A nasty little floater encountered at the beach or pool. See also MARCO POOLOO.

ud he'd tell everyone. He said the OZONE SLAYER smelt **151** times worse

T is for TUMMY TINKLE, a very polite way to describe having a big old spew.

TARANCHIHUAHUA

Depending who you ask, this is either the world's most terrifying dog or the world's cutest spider.

TAMING OF THE POO

A long-lost Shakespearean play about a poo so stubborn and headstrong that no one will marry it.

TEACH-ARGGGHS!, THE

An annual award for the world's worst teachers.

Did You Know?

TEACH-ARGGGHS! are awarded for detention-giving, bad breath, and unniceness. Other categories include the Bosscars (for bossiest teachers), the Failitzer (for most students failed), the Grannys (for oldest teacher), the ARIAs (Angry Redfaced Irritable Awards), and of course the coveted Nobell Prize (for teachers who ignore the bell). There are also honourable mentions for the M.B.V. (Most Boring Voice) and Golden Globs (most spitting whilst talking) awards. Last year's TEACH-ARGGGHS! champion was Mr Iwillonlysaythisonce from Fminusville who constructed an icosikaidigonal (22-sided) classroom so all his students could stand in a corner at the same time.

THINGFINDERER

Those magical people who are able to find things that are lost. They are experts at playing FINDCRAFT.

THONG-DO

An Australian martial arts variation of NANJITSU.

THUMBTWISTER

Parts in video games that are hard to get past. If there are too many of these in a row it may be you're playing a VIDEO LAME.

TIMBUCKLOO

A toilet so far away that it night as well be in Timbuktu.

THE TIM-TAMTRUM by BISCUITO PICASSO

TIM-TANTRUM

What happens when the Tim Tams run out.

TINKLER SPRINKLER

Someone who always misses the toilet bowl.

TISSUE ISSUE

What happens when you blow your nose too hard, bust through the paper and end up with snot on your hands. The first steps of the HANKYFANDANGO.

TOAD SIGNS

Road signs for toads.

CAUTION TADPOLES CROSSING

TOENAIL GUN

A gun that shoots toenails as bullets. Seriously dangerous and seriously smelly, it could never be classed as an UNDEADLY WEAPON.

TOESTACHE STYLES...

TOESTACHE

To trim your HAIRYFLOSS into a moustache shape.

TOO-LONG JOHNS

Undies you've had on for too long. These can be created when you are trying to use the LUCK OF THE DRAWERS too much.

TOOTIOUS MAXIMUS

A title given to the winner of a farting competition.

TROUBLE BUBBLE

The special place in the house where you can hide when you know you are going to get in trouble.

U

U is for UGLY CHUCKLING, a spew you think is going to be horrific but turns out to be SPEWTIFUL.

FAMOUS MODEL MOORANDA KERR

UDDER PANTS

Undies for cows.

COWVIN KLEINS

Matt! can
put our pants on?

WOO HOO!

CENSORED

UGG

A common name from the Stone Age. Also popular were Ogg, Nugg and Tony.

UME

An emu running backwards.

UNAMUSEMENT PARKS

These were invented by Walt Fizney, owner and proprietor of the world's first chain of the unsuccessful Fizneylands and the even more unsuccessful Euro Fizney. The queues are really long, the rides are super lame, and the 'you must be taller than this' signs are six feet tall so hardly anyone is allowed on.

UNDEADLY WEAPONS

Objects unlikely to kill your opponents. For example: feathers, paper aeroplanes, water pistols, snowballs and Dutch ovens.

UNDERSCARE

Having to wear someone else's undies.

UNEWESUAL

A weird sheep.

UNICORNY

Something so cutesy even a unicorn would find it too much, like a baby panda surfing a rainbow over a pink sparkling waterfall, with ponies.

UNIPSYCHO

A crazy person on a unicycle, best avoided. You should doubly avoid MANIYACK on a UNIPSYCHO.

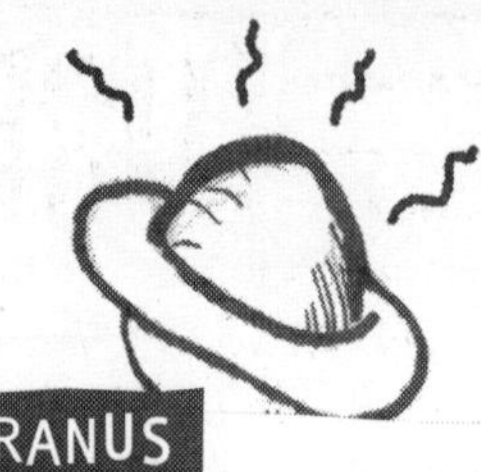

UN-NO-ABLE

Something that is impossible to say no to. Like buying a ticket in a GIRAFFLE, doing a DROP PLOP into a volcano or pressing buttons that say 'do not press'.

URANUS

Another of the incredibly smelly gas giant planets, Uranus smells so bad it was originally called Your and everybody else's anus but was shortened to 'ur anus' by ASSTRONOMERS for texting reasons. And the name stuck. Which is probably for the best.

URBANNED

To be banned from a city area. Often happens to busking FLOPERA SINGERS, aggressive pigeons, and UNIPSYCHOS.

URGENTS

What a man is looking for when he really needs to pee.

U.S.B.

Unbelievably Splashy Boogers. The way your snot goes really runny when you have a cold. Can be the cause of a DRIPSNIFF.

V

is for VOMCANO, when you lie on your back and vomit into the air.

VAMPIRE BATSPLAT

The embarrassing moment when a vampire in bat form accidentally flies into a closed window.

VACUCUMBER

The horrible cucumber-shaped lump of hair, carpet fuzz and dirt that clogs the vacuum cleaner hose. The main ingredient of vacucumber sandwiches, which taste a lot like a BRAT-WORST.

VAMPLETS

Baby vampires.

VAN GOTH

A gloomy painter who focused on nightscapes, velvet and dark black eye make-up.

VANISH

Something that is quite like a van but not. Like a ute, or a maxi taxi.

VEGEMIGHT?

A brown stain on your clothes that you hope is Vegemite.

VEGESCARIAN

Someone who is afraid of vegetables.

VELOCICRAPTOR

Someone who poos really fast.

VEIN BRAIN

A state of mind that vampires fall into when they are really hungry. Can happen directly after a VAMPIRE BATSPLAT.

VENOM-NOM-NOM

What snakes say when they are about to eat the prey they have just poisoned.

VENUS DI SMILO

A statue of the world's first ever smiley face, found in ancient Greece.

VERBURPS

Verbs are 'doing' words. Verburps are 'doing-while-burping' words.

VICTEARY

Crying when your team wins.

VIDEO LAME

A boring video game.

VIDEOSLIP

When you take a video instead of a photo on a smartphone.

– ever – along with a gang of **162** orangutans in an ORANGUTANGLE, with

Past Blast

VIKING KONGS, THE

A group of mad half-Swedish, half-Danish, half-gorilla warriors who terrorised Northern Europe in the old days. They liked raiding, singing, bananas, fighting, flat-pack furniture, hanging from buildings and wearing horned helmets. They were, like, the worst neighbours ever.

VIVA FREE WIRELESS!

An early song ELVIS PEASLEY wrote about the feeling you get when wi-fi is free. However, the song came out before the internet was invented so no one really knew what he was talking about and it flopped.

VLAD THE INHALER

The scourge of medieval Europe, VLAD THE INHALER was a generally nasty bloke who ran around stealing everyone's asthma puffers.

VOLCANOSE

When your nose erupts with so many U.S.Bs that you have a major TISSUE ISSUE and do the HANKYFANDANGO.

VOMITTENS

Gloves you use to pick up spew. You should also wear these when using a REPULSIEVE and should receive many YUCK BUCKS for your efforts.

VOODOO-DOO DOLL

When a witchdoctor steals a person's poo and uses it to sculpt a POOTRAIT of them. The doll is then used to control when that person needs to go to the toilet.

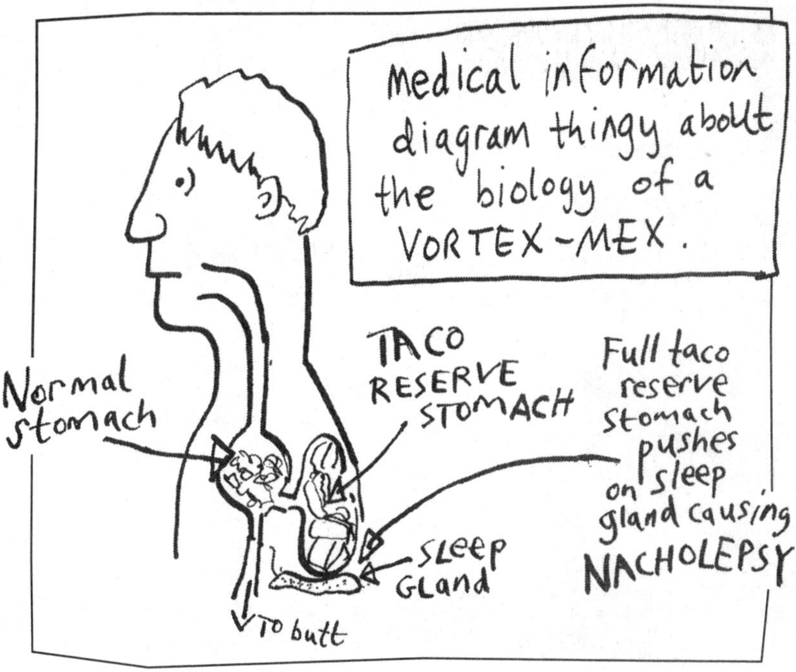

VORTEX-MEX

The weird ability you get on taco night to eat an impossible amount of tacos. A major cause of NACHOLEPSY.

VROOMBA

The world's fastest robot vacuum.

W is for WEIRD AND CHUNDERFUL, which is one way to describe all of the things you can see in vomit.

WALTZWAGON
A car that can dance.

WARTHOG
Someone who wants to have more warts than other people.

WATCHFROG
A frog specially trained to keep burglars out of your house.

WAXIDERMIST
People who make sculptures out of their ear wax.

WEETERNAL
A wee that goes on forever.

That's how bad it smelled. It was **166** million DECISMELLs, which is almost as

WEEHOUSE EFFECT

The theory that climate change will cause all the water in the rivers and seas to dry up. The only liquid left on earth will be wee. The sun will then evaporate the wee, which will cause yellow clouds and wee rain. Therefore, if the Weehouse Effect occurs you will be allowed to say, 'Wow, it is really p■■■■■g down today.'

WHALENTINES DAY

The most romantic day of the year for whales. As long as no one is in the KRILL ZONE, they have a whale of a time.

WHINING BOARD

A fold-out platform you stand at when you need to whine about doing chores.

WIG BANG, THE

A scientific theory used to explain the moment in time when wigs were invented. Proposed by famous ASSTRONOMER Stephen Mohawking.

Stephen Mohawking

WISHDOSHER

What it sounds like when you say 'dishwasher' after getting your mouth numbed at the dentist.

WIZZ FIZZ

The noise of wee meeting an electric fence.

*Warning! Trying this can result in having R.I.PEE on your gravestone.

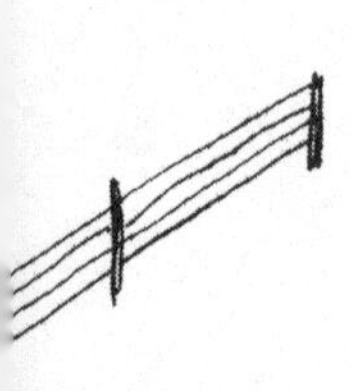

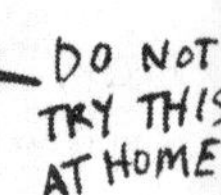

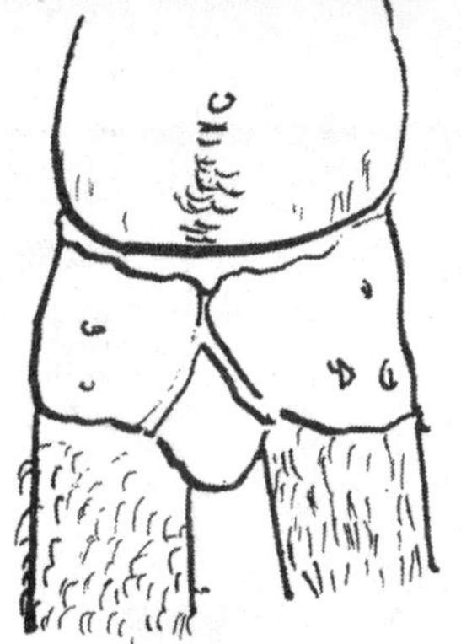

WHY-FRONTS?

Underwear that is so old, thin, baggy, stained and full of holes that they really should be thrown out. Similar to DAD SAGS.

Jane Ng
The girl with double WOBLES

WIZZLEFLOP

To wet the top bunk.

WOBLE

An elbow that can bend backwards. See also EENK.

WORST-AID KIT

A collection of useless things that are no help whatsoever in the event of an accident, like a ruler, a kayak, a whisk, boxing gloves, a bicycle pump, a trombone, a smoke machine and some wasps.

because it made the smell 169 times worse. Eventually a squad from

WORSTDAY PRESENT

A birthday present so bad it ruins the day.

WOWTER SPACE

The really cool parts of space. See also ASSTRONOMY.

WRECKTIFY

When you try and fix something by hitting it, but end up breaking it even more. Different but kind of similar to DESTRUCTIONS.

G.R.O.S.S.
Government Registry of Offendedness at Stupid Stories

D A N G E R

There are many words that start with the letter X. However, most of them are too revolting to be printed in a regular dictionary. Somehow The Listies have illegally obtained documents containing these words and printed them in this horrible book. Thankfully we at G.R.O.S.S. have censored these words, and their accompanying pictures, to protect the minds, hearts and eyes of children everywhere.

For your own safety, we strongly advise you skip the next six pages, as exposure to these words could cause nausea, vomiting, diarrhoea, motion sickness, sea sickness, something called BUMOURS, as well as really flakey dandruff. Better still, flush the whole book down the toilet where it belongs.

STOP READING

is for X YACKTOR, a TV talent show where contestants win if the judges throw up.

CAKE

The world's most disgusting cake. Half lamington and half [redacted] and covered in a [redacted] icing. See also LYCHEESE.

-A-MOBILE

When a baby does a poo in the car.

A [redacted] for your [redacted].

What you say when you realise you're too big to ride in shopping trolleys anymore.

The rudest word imaginable.

To eat [redacted] on [redacted] with a side of [redacted].

-A-MATIC

A fully robotic device for scraping off your shoe.

FACE

Something you should never call your brother or sister. Even when they are being a total FACE . For more fun ways to insult your siblings see our PATENTED RANDOM INSULT GENERATOR on page 176.

When something scares the out of you.

Something that smells like , looks like and feels like . Why? Because it is .

I DISAPPROVE OF SOME OF THESE WORDS! INFACT I DISAPPROVE OF ALL THESE WORDS! INFACT I DISAPPROVE OF EVERY █████ ONE OF THEM!

Mr B. Adbreath, Teacher.

| TOP 9 SWEAR WORDS |

█████: Never say this in class. You will be in detention until you retire.

█████!: What you yell when you get your ███ caught in your ████.

█████: A word so rude that when you say it birds fall out of the sky.

█: The world's shortest swear word.

██: The world's longest swear word.

██████ off!: How not to shoo away seagulls.

███'th: Swear word invented by William Shakespeare

Up ████ █████ creek: Much worse than any other creeks you may have heard of.

███ █████: This is secretly your nan's favourite swear word.

they held their noses praying that it would work. After **175** seconds, the missile exploded.

The Usties' Patented RANDOM INSULT GENERATOR

There are only so many times you can call someone a ██████FACE before it completely loses its impact. Luckily, we have invented a simple way to create new and interesting things to yell at people. Just roll three dice and use the handy table below to generate your insult.

Dice one	Dice two	Dice three
1. monkey	1. fart	1. lips
2. turkey	2. turd	2. face
3. donkey	3. spew	3. butt
4. duck	4. burp	4. nose
5. shark	5. phlegm	5. brains
6. dingo	6. snot	6. guts

monkey phlegm butt

ALSO WORKS WITH YOUR OWN WORDS!

XMASSACRE

Opening all your Christmas presents by tearing the paper in a mad rampage. See also RAPPING PAPER.

XMAS WEE

What Santa does in your toilet. FYI, Santa never flushes – he's too scared of waking up everyone in the house.

How mums can drink tea and coffee in like half a second.

Fireproof mouth Lining

1000°C

Fireproof neck

Fire proof guts.

XPRESSO

When your mum drinks her coffee super quickly.

XYLOPHOBIC

Being afraid of xylophones.

is for Y.O.L.L.O.: You Only Lose Lunch Once.

YADDA YADDA YODA

A wise old dude who won't shut up.

YADHTRIB TNESERP

The opposite of a birthday present. Similar but different to a WORSTDAY PRESENT.

Happy unbirthday!

YAXI DRIVER

Someone who drives yaks around. They are always happy to go to the HUNGRY YAKS drive thru.

YEARING AID

A device invented to help old people remember what year it is. Sometimes these are called 'calendars'.

YAXI
DRIVER
CAB
HONK! HONK!

YEAH-NAAAH

The polite way Australians say 'no' to doing something.

YOUR AND EVERYBODY ELSE'S ANUS

See URANUS.

to see if the area had to be quarantined for 178 months or not. It was very

YELLOW HEADLAND

Similar to a volcanic island, a Yellow Headland is caused when the earth develops a giant pus-filled pimple under the sea. The island appears as a large and angry-looking yellow and red mound in the middle of the ocean. If this sounds like a great place for a holiday to you, you may enjoy the DECAYMAN ISLANDS.

Did You Know?

Yellow Headlands are short-lived because the beaks of inquisitive seagulls tend to pop them. This causes massive pus explosions and tidal waves of foamy discharge. Notable Yellow Headlands include Mt Pusovius, Mt Zitna and Poppatoa. It is a natural phenomen so disgusting it has largely been kept under wraps by governments, historians and geography teachers.

YELLUE

An in-between colour, YELLUE Is a cross between yellow and blue. Other in-between colours are grink (green and pink), blaqua (black and aqua) and redurple (red and purple).

YEMPLETROMPING

The scientific name of the game where you avoid stepping on the cracks in the pavement. Excessive YEMPLETROMPING may get you URBANNED.

YESTERMORROW

Another word for today.

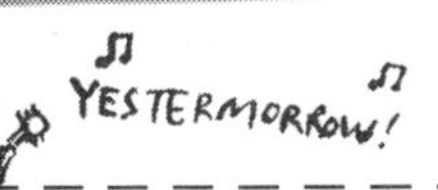

Y-FONTS

A font that can be used to write your name on your undies. Popular Y-FONTS are Times Poo Roman, Pongic Sans and Smelvetica.

YIPPEAS

Peas that are excited to be eaten.

YOINK

What someone says when they nick food from your plate.

YOGAS

Farting whilst doing yoga.

saying it was all clear. A huge cheer went up from the **180** thousand people who had been evacuated.

YOLKO ONO

A famous chicken performance artist. Said to be a descendent of CLUCKOPATRA.

Y.O.L.O. (You Only Loo Once)

A phrase used by irate parents on long car trips. It means that there will only be one toilet stop, and it's now, so even if you don't think you need to go, you should go, because Y.O.L.O. It is helpful in this case to be a VELOCICRAPTOR.

YO-NO

Tying a string to something in an attempt to turn it into a yo-yo.

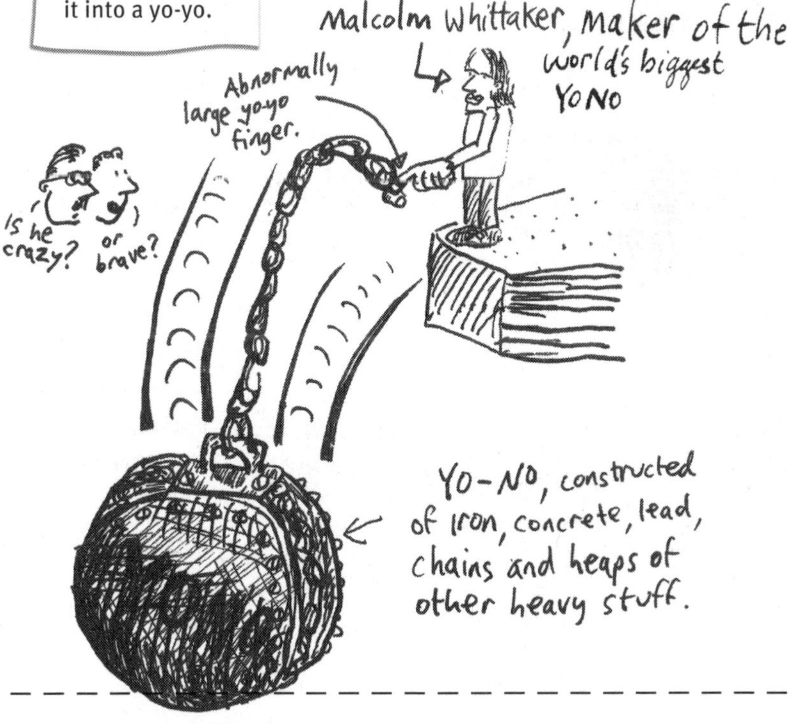

Malcolm Whittaker, maker of the world's biggest YONO

Abnormally large yo-yo finger.

Is he crazy?

or brave?

YO-NO, constructed of iron, concrete, lead, chains and heaps of other heavy stuff.

YOT

How yacht is spelt in INGLISH.

YOODLES

A measurement on the U.D.O.N. scale (Dr. Umami's Density Of Noodles) that measures how many noodles there are.

THE U·D·O·N· SCALE

OODLES

SQUOODLES

GOODLES

DOODLES

ZOODLES

YOODLES

DEEP END

man said. 'It was nearly as good as the **182**nd annual HOOTENGRANNY.' No one is sure whether to

YOUGHURT

Yoghurt you make yourself. A fool-proof recipe: Take one bottle of milk. Place it on top of a heater. Wait 6 to 7 weeks. Eat.

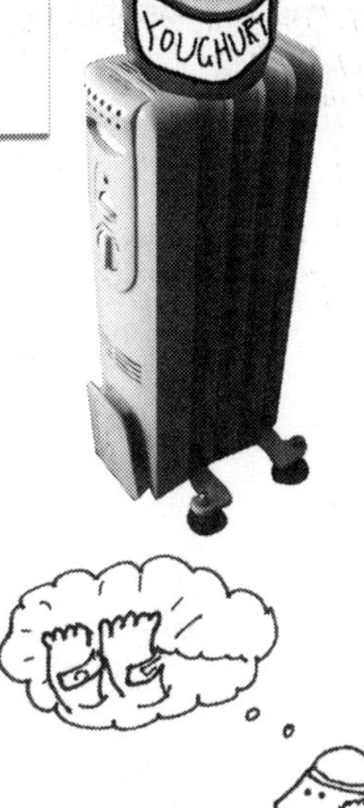

YOUREEKA!

What you yell when you discover that your, or someone else's, feet stink. See also BLISTORY.

YUCK BUCKS

Money you earn for doing something gross. Like being made to clean a SARCOUGHYGAS when a BLUNDERBUTT in EGGMODE is blasting OZONE SLAYERS inside the world's most toxic NOSE-GO ZONE. That, or having to drink a BIN JUICE milkshake.

believe this story. The old man's LIE-Q is 183, which means we'll never know if it really was the

Z is for ZIP-A-DEE-DOO-BARF, a song you sing into the toilet bowl to try and cheer yourself up between spews.

ZAGZAG

When a zigzag has too much zag and not enough zig. The opposite of a zigzig, which is when a zigzag has too much zig and not enough zag.

ZALKING

The way a person walks when they wear high heels for the first time. Never try YEMPLETROMPING and ZALKING at the same time.

ZAP ATTACK

Using static electricity to give someone an electric shock.

ZZZZZZZZZZZZZZZZ

ZEALAND

A country where everything starts with Z. Singing is called zinging, pigs say zoink! Shoes are called zhoes and monks are called zonks. The Zing and Zueen are called Zob and Zarah Zg. If you are ALLETTERGIC to the letter Z you should avoid going here because you will zneeze a lot, using up many zankies and covering zeveryone with znot. Some Zealanders got zick of saying Z all the zime and zailed acrozz the zea to ztart a new country called New Zealand. Even though not everything starts with a Z there, they still talk differently.

ZEBRAS

Good for keeping zeboobs in.

ZEST OF A LEMMING

To shave a lemming's fur and use it in cakes, jams and drinks. An acquired taste.

THE ANTI LEMMING ZEST LOBBY.

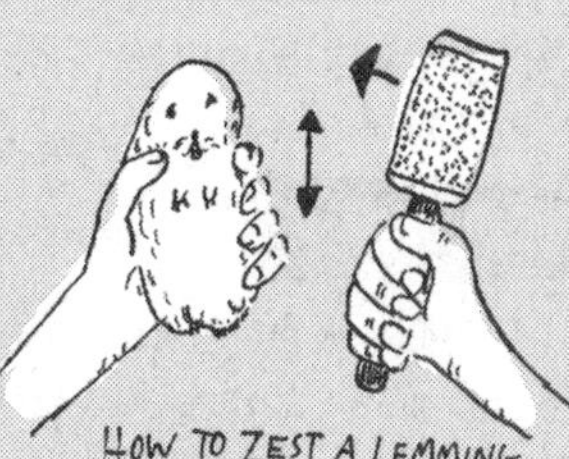

HOW TO ZEST A LEMMING. (PLEASE ASK LEMMING'S PERMISSION FIRST)

THE CONTROVERSIAL PRACTICE OF LEMMING ZESTING.

Except, of course there is also **185**. But it is the last one. Definitely. Goodbye …

ZILLIONGABILLION

The largest number it is possible to count up to in a human lifetime, provided you don't get COUNTSTIPATED.

ZILLIONS

A lot of lions.

ZINKLEGRITTING

Chewing tin foil to freak people out.

ZIPLOCK BRAG

An air-tight exaggeration.

ZIPSPLODE

The embarrassing moment when the fly on a pair of pants completely fails and has to be fixed with anything at hand, such as sticky tape, dental floss or a safety pin (risky!).

ZITERATURE

Books about pimples.

ZIT WIT

Someone with pus for brains.

ZODIYACK

To talk too much about star-signs. Interestingly a lot of VEGISCARIANS engage in ZODIYACK.

there is of course **187**, which we always forget about. So that's the last number.

ZOMBA

An exercise class especially for zombies.

ARE YOU A ZOMBIE?

1. What do people say when you walk in the door?

A 'Hello, <insert name here>.'

B 'Hello, Insertnamehere.' Because you recently changed your name to Insertnamehere just to be annoying.

C 'Argh! Destroy its brain! Destroy its brain! Cut off its head! Ruuun!'

2. What's your favourite thing to eat?

A Fruit.

B Everything, like literally everything. Apart from broccoli.

C BRAAAAINS!

Laterz. You can stop reading. But only after you've read page **188** That's definitely it. *Finito*. The end. All over.

Happy Brainday card

Zombie smiling (hard to tell because his face is rotting)

3. You just realised it's your mum's birthday and you forgot to get her a card. You:

A Run to the milk bar and buy her a card.

B Steam open your sister's/brother's card, rub out their name and replace it with your own.

C Run around the house knocking things over, trying to eat people and yelling, 'BRAAAAAINS!'

4. Does your breath smell of:

A Minty freshness.

B Sort've like cheese, sort've like pickled onions.

C BRAAAAINS!

5. What are your favourite clothes?

A The clothes you wore to the school formal.

B Underpants, unwashed and on the outside.

C The rotting, decaying clothes you died in.

Some flowers

6. Complete this poem:
Roses are red, violets are blue…

A So are your eyes, and I love you.

B Poops are brown and they belong in the loo.

C BRAAAAINS!

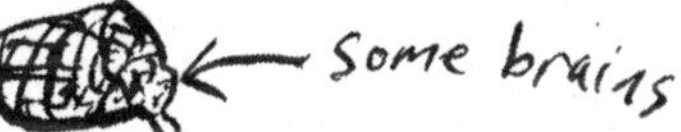

Some poop

7. The old man next door needs help with his shopping. Do you:

A Help him carry the shopping, whilst skipping alongside and singing a happy song.

B Eat as much of the shopping as possible, making the bags lighter to carry.

C Chase the old man down the street and attempt to eat his brains.

8. What is six minus two?

A What a lovely question. Four.

B Err, maths?

C BRAAAINNS!

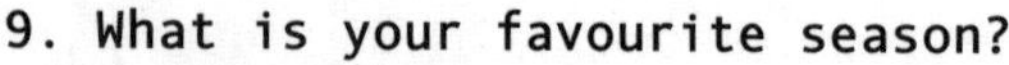

9. What is your favourite season?

A Spring? Summer? Actually, winter and autumn are also nice in their own ways.

B Waterbomb season, booby trap season and a bunch of other seasons I invented.

C BRAAAINS!

10. What is your favourite thing to do on the weekend?

A Pick flowers, do homework and chase butterflies.

B Set booby-traps for siblings, attempt dangerous stunts and poke dog poop with sticks.

C Eat brains.

So are you a Zombie? What is your score?

Mostly As: Not a Zombie.

Mostly Bs: Not a Zombie.

Mostly Cs: Brains brains brains brains brains, brain brains. Brains brains brains. Brains. Brains brains brains brains brains, brain brains. Brains brains brains. Brains.

Next you will say there is a number **190**, which is a crazy idea, because

ZOMBAMBI

The sequel to Bambi. Mum's back and she wants revenge!

ZOODLING

Drawing animals that don't exist.

ZQXJKYW

A word invented in order to cheat at Scrabble. See also ██████.

ZUCCHINI BIKINI

A swimsuit made of vegetables.

ZUCCHOUTI

The opposite of a zucchini.

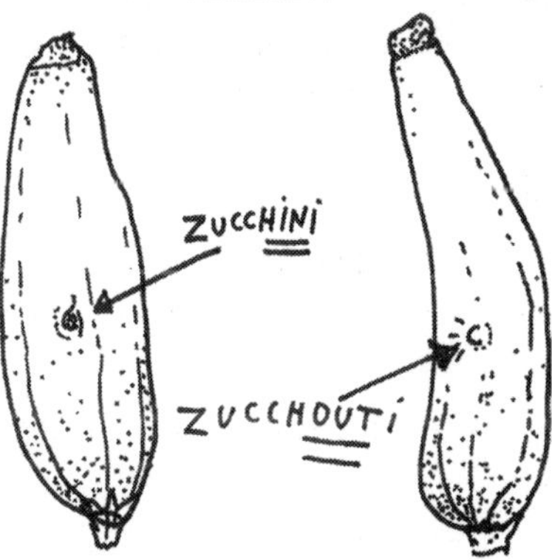

ZZZEND

To fall asleep before the end of something, like during a movie, reading a book or writing this senten

Well done! You have read all the way to the end of ICKYPEDIA.

But how well have you been paying attention?

TAKE THE ICKYPEDIA QUIZ!

1. The first poo you do in the morning is called a:

A COCK-A-DOODLE POO
B ALARM PLOP
C BREAKFAST BROWNIE
D TOAST FLOAT

2. YUCK BUCKS is money you earn for:

A squeezing the pimples on your dad/mum's back
B clearing up dried dog poo in the back-yard
C changing a baby's nappy
D all of the above

3. When is your HALFDAY?

A halfway through your birthday day
B halfway between your birthday and Christmas
C the day exactly halfway between your last birthday and your next
D six days before the yesterday's yesterday's tomorrow's next weekend

4. You have just won the lottery and decided to start your own circus. Which animal would make the best attraction?

A IGUANANA
B ORANGUTANGLE
C ACROCAT
D SPIHIDER

5. Your aunty is a CHEEKFREAK. This means she:

A compulsively slaps people on the bum

B compulsively slaps her own bum

C compulsively slaps other people with her bum

D compulsively kisses on the cheek to say 'hello'

---

6. An E-SNAIL is:

A a snail who's good with computers

B someone with really slow internet speed

C a person who is always late answering emails

D a robotic snail that delivers letters

---

7. Is a HOOTENGRANNY:

A a part grandmother, part owl mutant hybrid

B a nan who does bird impressions

C an event where grandmothers have lots of fun

D a nan who is nocturnal, lives in a tree and hunts mice

---

8. How do you spell turtle in INGLISH:

A tertal

B turtel

C terrrrrrrrrrrrrrrrrrrrrtle

D all of the above

9. Which of the following are not INVENTSHUNS?

A FIREY FLOSS: Fairy floss you set on fire before you eat it

B NUCLEARINGS: Radioactive earrings

C BIÑATAS: piñatas full of rubbish

D ROLLER TOASTER: A toaster on wheels that hurtles around your kitchen looping the loop until your bread is browned

---

10. What is the term for burping like someone else?

A A BURPYCAT DOPPLEBELCHER

B IMBURPANATION

C BELCHICOPTER

D ECHO NO-NO

---

11. Which word does not appear in ICKYPEDIA?

A ROBUTT

B QLEVER

C LOLLIPLOP

D PUS FUSS

---

12. Which of the following is not an UNDEADLY WEAPON?

A a feather

B a soft toothbrush

C a cloud

D a huge concrete feather covered in sharpened toothbrushes dropped from a cloud

ANSWERS
1.A 2.D 3.C 4.C 5.D 6.C
7.C 8.D 9.D 10.B 11.D 12.D

THE END-OF-ICKYPEDIA READER SURVEY

You have reached the end of the book. How do you feel?

A Smart, learned, educated.

B Oh, is this the end? I must be reading it back to front.

C Hungry for more book.

Did you have a favourite word?

A Yes. But it's a secret...

B I don't know, I haven't read it yet. I just said that.

C Hee Haw!

Do you have any ideas for your own words?

A Yes, heaps!

B No, not yet. I told you I haven't read it!

C I'm hungry. Have you got any more books?

Was this book too icky?

A Yes, but I loved every minute of it.

B SERIOUSLY STOP ASKING ME QUESTIONS I HAVE NOT READ IT!

C No, it was quite the opposite. It tasted great.

- -

Do you have any suggestions for the authors for their next book?

A Keep doing what you're doing, you are amazing.

B RIGHT! I HAVE HAD ENOUGH OF ALL THIS! STOP ASKING ME ██████ QUESTIONS! I DON'T CARE ABOUT THIS █████ BOOK! I'M GOING!

C Yes, could the next one have a bit of ketchup and maybe mustard on it?

Who are you?

A I am me, and this is my ICKYPEDIA.

B "Hello, I'm not here right now, but please leave your name and number and I'll get back to you when I can ... BEEEEEEP!"

C A donkey.

Mostly As: You read the book, thanks. If you have any suggestions for the book why not write to Matt and Rich? hello@thelisties.com

Mostly Bs: You have not read the book. You have already left and are not reading this part of the survey either.

Mostly Cs: You are a donkey, you ate the book, saved the last page and read this survey. You will now probably eat this survey.

Ac-knowl-edge-ments

Here is one final list: A ZILLIONGABILLION thank-yous go out to Vanessa Rouse and Toby Sullivan, Jane Godwin, Bruno Herfst, Kate O'Donnell, Katrina, Clair and all at Penguin Books, Lynne Ellis, Andrew Callaghan, our families (mums, dads, brothers, sisters and boxheads), MG, The Malthouse Theatre, all of the theatres and festivals that invite us to play and – most totes importanté – all of the Listeroonies who come to see our shows.

About the Authors

Richard Higgins and Matt Kelly are The Listies, a duo who perform comedy for kids and their adults. They met back in the dinosaur times when they were cast as Mr and Mrs Twit in the RMIT kids show by Lynne Ellis, and

in 2008 they made their first show together. Since then they have made seven shows, two albums and toured all over the place, including South Korea, Scotland and Wollongong — they've won a bunch of awards too. ICKYPEDIA is their first book.

PLEASE NOTE

If you think anything in ICKYPEDIA is too disgusting then please write your complaint in detail on a piece of toilet paper and flush it down the loo. Our complaints department will deal with it down there.